TurnAround

PROGRAM COOKBOOK

125 EASY RECIPES FOR BOTH THE
Flex AND **Core Plans**

TurnAround Icon Key:

 CORE PLAN RECIPE

 SPICY

NO COOK

ONE POT

20 MINUTES OR LESS

VEGETARIAN

A Word About Weight Watchers

Since 1963, Weight Watchers has grown from a handful of members to millions of enrollments annually. Today Weight Watchers is recognized as the leading name in safe and sensible weight control. Weight Watchers members are a diverse group, from youths to senior citizens, attending meetings virtually around the globe. Weight-loss and weight-management results vary by individual, but we recommend that you attend Weight Watchers meetings, follow the Weight Watchers food plan, and participate in regular physical activity. For the Weight Watchers meeting nearest you, call 800-651-6000. Also, visit us at our Web site, **WeightWatchers.com**, or look for *Weight Watchers* Magazine at your newsstand or in your meeting room.

Grilled Thai Beef Salad, page 53

WEIGHT WATCHERS PUBLISHING GROUP

CREATIVE AND EDITORIAL DIRECTOR: **NANCY GAGLIARDI**

ART DIRECTOR: **ED MELNITSKY**

PRODUCTION MANAGER: **ALAN BIEDERMAN**

ASSOCIATE ART DIRECTOR: **JENNIFER BOWLES**

OFFICE MANAGER AND PUBLISHING ASSISTANT: **JENNY LABOY-BRACE**

EDITOR: **EILEEN RUNYAN**

FOOD EDITOR: **CAROL PRAGER**

RECIPE DEVELOPERS: **DAVID BONOM, TERRY GRIECO KENNY, LORI LONGBOTHAM**

NUTRITION CONSULTANT: **PATTY SANTELLI**

PHOTOGRAPHER: **RITA MAAS**

FOOD STYLIST: **MICHAEL PEDERSON**

PROP STYLIST: **BETTE BLAU**

DESIGN/PRODUCTION: **LYNDA D'AMICO**

ON THE COVER: Spaghetti Bolognese, page 82 (with a *POINTS*® value of only 8)

Introduction

Get ready to cook with Weight Watchers exciting **TurnAround** program. Our new program incorporates the essentials for successful weight loss: healthy nutrition, effective calorie control, livability, and so much more.

With its two food plans, the **Core Plan** and the **Flex Plan**, the **TurnAround** program recognizes that there can be different approaches to losing weight in a healthy and satisfying way.

The *TurnAround Program Cookbook* was created with both of these food plans in mind. Knowing that you may be following either of the two plans, we designed this cookbook to fulfill all of your recipe needs. Before you get cooking with these delicious recipes, here are a few things to keep in mind:

- All 125 recipes can be used for both the **Core Plan** and the **Flex Plan.**
- If a recipe includes a serving suggestion for a food that isn't on the **Core Food List,** we've included the additional *POINTS* value for that food. So, if you're following the **Core Plan,** be sure to deduct those *POINTS* values from your **weekly *POINTS* Allowance.** And, if you're following the **Flex Plan,** be sure to add those additional *POINTS* values to the per serving *POINTS* value.
- If you're following the **Core Plan,** we specifically created the recipes to help you monitor the amount of healthy oil you're eating each day. If you prepare any recipe that includes oil (olive, canola, safflower, sunflower, or flaxseed) in its ingredients, please note that we've used no more than one teaspoon of oil per serving per recipe.

In this cookbook, you'll discover 125 new ways to prepare delicious meals. We hope that you'll enjoy cooking with the **TurnAround** program.

Crispy Sweet-Potato "Fries", page 154
and Spicy Potato Sticks, page 156

Contents

CHAPTER 1

Morning Meals and Lunch Specials

Solo Veggie Omelette

Whipping up an omelette for one is a good meal plan anytime of day. Our version features onions and bell peppers, but you can substitute ¹/₄ cup chopped shiitake mushrooms for the bell peppers for a different tasty filling.

1. Spray a small nonstick omelette pan with canola oil nonstick spray and set over medium heat. Add the onion and bell pepper; cook, stirring frequently, until tender, about 5 minutes. Transfer the vegetables to a plate and set aside.

2. Beat the egg, egg whites, and water in a small bowl until frothy.

3. Heat the oil in the omelette pan until a drop of water sizzles on it. Pour in the egg mixture and swirl to cover the pan. Cook, stirring gently, until the underside is set, about 1 minute. Sprinkle the onion and bell pepper evenly over half the omelette; fold the other half over the filling. Slide the omelette onto a plate; sprinkle with the salt and pepper.

PER SERVING: 170 Cal, 8 g Fat, 2 g Sat Fat, 0 g Trans Fat, 213 mg Chol, 757 mg Sod, 11 g Carb, 2 g Fib, 15 g Prot, 51 mg Calc. **POINTS** value: **4.**

★

★ **tip** For an herb omelette, beat 1 teaspoon chopped fresh parsley, 1 teaspoon snipped fresh chives, and ¹/₄ teaspoon chopped fresh thyme into the egg mixture in step 2.

MAKES 1 SERVING

½ **onion**, chopped

¼ **red bell pepper**, seeded and chopped

1 large **egg**

2 **egg whites**

2 tablespoons **water**

½ teaspoon **canola oil**

¼ teaspoon **salt**

¼ teaspoon freshly **ground pepper**

Tomato and Spinach Omelette

If you use packaged baby spinach for this recipe, you'll need to rinse it first in a colander before adding it to the saucepan in step 1. It will need the water clinging to its leaves to wilt properly. Never make an omelette with more than 3 eggs. If you're serving more than one person, make a separate omelette for each one.

1. Heat a medium saucepan over medium-high heat. Add the spinach with just the water that clings to it; cook, stirring constantly, until just wilted, about 2 minutes. Drain well, squeezing out all the liquid. Cool slightly, then chop finely.

2. Beat the eggs, salt, pepper, and water in a small bowl until frothy.

3. Heat the oil in a small omelette pan until a drop of water sizzles on it. Pour in the egg mixture and swirl to cover the pan. Reduce the heat and cook until the underside is set and the top is a little creamy, about 2 minutes. Sprinkle the spinach and tomato evenly over half the omelette; fold the other half over the filling. Cook until the omelette is completely set, about 1 minute longer. To serve, slide the omelette onto a plate.

PER SERVING: 206 Cal, 13 g Fat, 4 g Sat Fat, 0 g Trans Fat, 425 mg Chol, 786 mg Sod, 8 g Carb, 3 g Fib, 16 g Prot, 131 mg Calc. **POINTS** value: **5.**

★

★ **tip** If you like, add freshly grated Parmesan cheese to the beaten-egg mixture (1 tablespoon will increase the **POINTS** value by 1).

MAKES 1 SERVING

2½ cups coarsely chopped cleaned **spinach**, (do not dry)

2 large **eggs**

¼ teaspoon **salt**

¼ teaspoon freshly **ground pepper**

1 tablespoon **water**

½ teaspoon **olive oil**

1 small **tomato**, diced

Italian Potato and Artichoke Frittata

Italian Potato and Artichoke Frittata

This hearty frittata, with red potatoes, scallions, and artichoke hearts, is a perfect choice if you've invited company for brunch. Serve with a crisp mesclun salad.

1. Preheat the oven to 375°F. In a medium bowl, beat the eggs, egg whites, salt, pepper, and water.

2. Heat the oil in a medium nonstick skillet with an ovenproof handle over medium-low heat. Add the artichoke hearts, scallions, and Italian herb seasoning; cook, stirring occasionally, until softened, about 5 minutes. Stir in the potatoes.

3. Add the egg mixture and cook stirring until the eggs just begin to set, about 2 minutes. If necessary, evenly distribute the vegetables in the pan and cook, without stirring, until the eggs are almost set, 5–6 minutes. Transfer the skillet to the oven and bake until the eggs are completely set in the center, 5–6 minutes. Invert and cut into 4 wedges.

PER SERVING (1 WEDGE): 157 Cal, 4 g Fat, 1 g Sat Fat, 0 g Trans Fat, 106 mg Chol, 496 mg Sod, 20 g Carb, 2 g Fib, 10 g Prot, 34 mg Calc. *POINTS* value: *3*.

★
★ **tip** If you don't have Italian herb seasoning on hand, use an equal amount of dried thyme or basil.

MAKES 4 SERVINGS

2 large **eggs**

4 **egg whites**

½ teaspoon **salt**

¼ teaspoon freshly **ground pepper**

2 tablespoons **water**

1 teaspoon **olive oil**

1½ cups rinsed canned **artichoke hearts**, cut into wedges

3 **scallions**, sliced

¾ teaspoon **Italian herb seasoning**

2 small **red potatoes**, cooked and thinly sliced

Potato and Bell-Pepper Frittata with Thyme

Like all frittatas, this one can be served immediately. If you prefer, you can make it up to 1 hour ahead of time, let it cool in the pan, and serve it at room temperature.

1. Heat the oil in a medium nonstick skillet with an ovenproof handle over medium heat. Add the bell peppers, onion, and garlic; cook, stirring occasionally, until softened, 7–8 minutes. Stir in the potato and thyme; cook, stirring occasionally, about 5 minutes.

2. Preheat the broiler. In a small bowl, lightly beat the eggs, egg whites, salt, and pepper; pour over the vegetables, stirring gently to combine. Reduce the heat and cook, without stirring, until the eggs are set, 12–15 minutes. Place the frittata in the skillet under the broiler and broil until the top is lightly browned, about 2 minutes. Let stand 5 minutes before serving.

PER SERVING (¼ OF FRITTATA): 196 Cal, 8 g Fat, 2 g Sat Fat, 0 g Trans Fat, 212 mg Chol, 390 mg Sod, 22 g Carb, 5 g Fib, 12 g Prot, 57 mg Calc. *POINTS* value: *4.*

MAKES 4 SERVINGS

- 2 teaspoons **olive oil**
- 2 **red bell peppers**, seeded and thinly sliced
- 1 **onion**, thinly sliced
- 2 **garlic cloves**, minced
- 1 small **all-purpose potato**, cooked and thinly sliced
- ½ teaspoon **dried thyme**, crumbled
- 4 large **eggs**
- 2 **egg whites**
- ½ teaspoon **salt**
- ¼ teaspoon freshly **ground pepper**

Creamy Cheese Rotini with Garlic and Oil

Your guests will never believe that this creamy, rich-tasting pasta is made with fat-free ricotta and mozzarella cheeses. Our trick is to toss the still-hot pasta first with garlicky olive oil, then stir in the cheeses until they melt. Don't let the amount of garlic throw you; its flavor sweetens and mellows when sautéed until golden. But if you're feeling cautious, use half the amount.

1. Cook the rotini according to package directions. Drain and set aside.

2. Meanwhile, combine the ricotta and mozzarella cheeses in a small bowl.

3. Heat the oil in a large saucepan over medium-high heat. Add the garlic and cook, stirring constantly, until lightly golden and fragrant, about 1 minute. Add the rotini and cook, stirring constantly, until well coated, about 30 seconds. Add the cheeses and cook, stirring occasionally, until melted and creamy, about 2 minutes. Remove the skillet from the heat. Stir in the tomatoes, basil, salt, and pepper.

PER SERVING (1¼ CUPS): 370 Cal, 6 g Fat, 1 g Sat Fat, 0 g Trans Fat, 18 mg Chol, 618 mg Sod, 55 g Carb, 8 g Fib, 25 g Prot, 592 mg Calc. **POINTS** value: **7.**

★

★ **tip** This recipe works just as well with whole-wheat penne or fusilli.

MAKES 4 SERVINGS

½ pound **whole-wheat rotini**

1½ cups **fat-free ricotta cheese**

1 cup shredded **fat-free mozzarella cheese**

4 teaspoons **extra-virgin olive oil**

6 **garlic cloves**, thinly sliced

3 **plum tomatoes**, chopped

½ cup thinly sliced **fresh basil**

½ teaspoon **salt**

¼ teaspoon freshly **ground pepper**

Sautéed Chicken Breasts with Plum Salsa

Great in the summer and in the fall when plums are at their best, this is a simple and gorgeous chicken dish—and the salsa is great with pork tenderloin, too. You can also use fresh apricots, peaches, or nectarines instead of plums. Serve with tossed greens, if desired.

1. To make the salsa, combine the plums, onion, bell pepper, jalapeño, cilantro, oil, vinegar, ⅛ teaspoon of the salt, and ⅛ teaspoon of the pepper in a medium bowl; set aside.

2. Sprinkle the chicken with the remaining ⅛ teaspoon salt and ⅛ teaspoon pepper. Spray a large nonstick skillet with canola oil nonstick spray and set over medium heat. Add the chicken and cook, turning once, until cooked through, 10–12 minutes. Serve with the plum salsa.

PER SERVING (1 PIECE CHICKEN WITH ⅔ CUP SALSA): 180 Cal, 4 g Fat, 1 g Sat Fat, 0 g Trans Fat, 63 mg Chol, 201 mg Sod, 11 g Carb, 1 g Fib, 24 g Prot, 15 mg Calc. *POINTS* value: **4.**

★

★ **tip** If you're buying plums to use the same day, it's best to look for fruit that is soft, gives to gentle pressure with the palm of the hand, and has a sweet aroma. To ripen plums, place the fruit in a paper bag, fold the top over loosely, and keep at room temperature for 1 to 3 days. Check daily. (Avoid using a plastic bag, as it retains moisture, which may cause the fruit to decay.)

MAKES 4 SERVINGS 🔥 🕐

- 4 red and/or purple **plums**, pitted and chopped

- ¼ cup finely chopped **red onion**

- ¼ cup seeded and finely chopped **yellow bell pepper**

- 1 **jalapeño pepper**, seeded and finely chopped (wear gloves to prevent irritation)

- 2 tablespoons finely chopped **fresh cilantro**

- 1 teaspoon **sunflower oil**

- 1 teaspoon **rice vinegar**

- ¼ teaspoon **salt**

- ¼ teaspoon freshly **ground pepper**

- 4 (¼-pound) skinless boneless **chicken breast** halves, trimmed of all visible fat

Sautéed Chicken Breasts
with Plum Salsa

Chopped Salad with Tuna and White Beans

Chopped Salad with Tuna and White Beans

Leave it to the Italians to concoct a winning combination like tuna and white beans. We take this classic one step further by incorporating shredded romaine, peppery arugula, and crunchy veggies. The flaxseed oil in the vinaigrette dressing adds a terrific flavor—much like that of pecans.

Whisk the broth, shallots, parsley, oil, vinegar, mustard, salt, and pepper in a large bowl. Add the lettuce and remaining ingredients; toss to coat with the dressing. Serve at once or cover and refrigerate for up to 30 minutes.

PER SERVING (2½ CUPS): 214 Cal, 7 g Fat, 1 g Sat Fat, 0 g Trans Fat, 30 mg Chol, 650 mg Sod, 21 g Carb, 6 g Fib, 23 g Prot, 100 mg Calc. *POINTS* value: *4.*

★

★ tip Flaxseed oil is the best available plant source of omega-3 fatty acids and, according to the U.S. Department of Agriculture, contains cancer-fighting agents. You can buy flaxseed oil in health-food stores and in an increasing number of supermarkets. Because it is extremely susceptible to damage by heat, light, and oxygen, it is packaged in black or brown bottles and refrigerated. Check the sell-by date and once you get it home, store it in your refrigerator, where it will stay fresh for 2 to 3 months. If you think you won't use it within that time, pop the bottle in the freezer, where it will last for about a year. Flaxseed oil should not be exposed to direct heat, as in sautéing, as that will damage the oil. It's great in salad dressings, however.

MAKES 4 SERVINGS

½ cup reduced-sodium **chicken broth**

2 **shallots**, finely chopped

3 tablespoons chopped flat-leaf **parsley**

1 tablespoon **flaxseed oil** (See Tip.)

2 teaspoons **balsamic vinegar**

1 teaspoon **Dijon mustard**

¼ teaspoon **salt**

¼ teaspoon freshly **ground pepper**

3 cups finely shredded **romaine lettuce**

3 cups finely shredded **arugula** leaves

3 **plum tomatoes**, seeded and finely chopped

2 (6-ounce) cans water-packed **tuna**, drained

2 **assorted color bell peppers**, seeded and finely chopped

1 cup canned **white beans**, rinsed and drained

1 small **red onion**, finely chopped

Salmon with Spinach, Tomatoes, and Dill-Mustard Sauce

We pan-sear the salmon fillets to render some of their natural oils, then sauté the shallots, garlic, tomatoes, and spinach in the same skillet so the vegetables pick up a delicious light salmon flavor.

1. To make the dill-mustard sauce, combine the sour cream, mustard, dill, and lemon juice in a small bowl; set aside.

2. Sprinkle the salmon with ½ teaspoon of the salt and ⅛ teaspoon of the pepper. Spray a large nonstick skillet with olive oil nonstick spray and set over medium-high heat. Add the salmon and cook until golden and just opaque in the center, 5–6 minutes on each side. Transfer the salmon to a platter; cover to keep warm.

3. Add the shallots and garlic to the skillet; cook, stirring constantly, until fragrant, about 30 seconds. Add the tomatoes and cook, stirring occasionally, until they begin to soften, 1–2 minutes. Add the spinach and cook, tossing frequently, until wilted, 1–2 minutes. Stir in the remaining ½ teaspoon salt and ⅛ teaspoon pepper. Serve the salmon with the spinach mixture and the dill-mustard sauce.

PER SERVING (1 SALMON FILLET WITH ¾ CUP SPINACH AND TOMATOES AND 2 TABLESPOONS SAUCE): 238 Cal, 4 g Fat, 1 g Sat Fat, 0 g Trans Fat, 70 mg Chol, 949 mg Sod, 19 g Carb, 4 g Fib, 30 g Prot, 135 mg Calc. *POINTS* value: **4.**

★

★ **tip** Serve this dish with brown rice (½ cup cooked brown rice for each serving will increase the *POINTS* value by 2).

MAKES 4 SERVINGS 🍳

½ cup **fat-free sour cream**

4 teaspoons **whole-grain mustard**

1 tablespoon chopped **fresh dill**

1 teaspoon **fresh lemon juice**

4 (¼-pound) skinless **salmon fillets**

1 teaspoon **salt**

¼ teaspoon freshly **ground pepper**

⅓ cup chopped **shallots**

2 **garlic cloves**, minced

1 pint **grape tomatoes**

1 (10-ounce) bag triple-washed fresh **spinach**

Crispy Potato-Zucchini Pancakes

The good news is that adding zucchini to potato pancakes not only cuts calories but also adds moisture and tenderness, which is especially important when you're cooking with a trace amount of oil.

1. Toss the potatoes, zucchini, and salt in a medium bowl. Let stand 10 minutes. Squeeze out the liquids and discard. Stir in the egg, scallions, cornmeal, tarragon, and pepper.

2. Heat ¼ teaspoon of the oil in a large nonstick skillet over medium heat. Drop half of the potato mixture, 2 tablespoons at a time, into mounds and flatten with a spatula. Cook until lightly browned, about 12 minutes, turning and adding another ¼ teaspoon oil after 6 minutes. Repeat with the remaining oil and the potato mixture to make a total of 8 pancakes. Top each pancake with ½ teaspoon of sour cream.

PER SERVING (2 PANCAKES): 127 Cal, 3 g Fat, 1 g Sat Fat, 0 g Trans Fat, 53 mg Chol, 469 mg Sod, 22 g Carb, 3 g Fib, 4 g Prot, 38 mg Calc. **POINTS** value: **2**.

★

★ **tip** These pancakes are also delicious served with unsweetened applesauce instead of sour cream.

MAKES 4 SERVINGS 🥕

2 large **russet potatoes** (about 1½ pounds), peeled and shredded (about 2 cups)

2 medium **zucchini**, shredded (about 2 cups)

¾ teaspoon **salt**

1 large **egg**

3 **scallions**, sliced

2 tablespoons **cornmeal**

½ teaspoon **dried tarragon**, crumbled

⅛ teaspoon freshly **ground pepper**

1 teaspoon **olive oil**

4 teaspoons **fat-free sour cream**

Corn and Black-Bean Lettuce Bundles

Take advantage of fresh corn in season by cutting the kernels from an ear of cooked corn for this recipe. Otherwise, canned or frozen corn is a fine substitute.

1. In a medium bowl, combine the beans, corn, bell pepper, scallions, cilantro, lime juice, oil, cumin, garlic, and salt. Refrigerate, covered, at least 1 hour to allow the flavors to blend.

2. Place a lettuce leaf on a work surface and spoon about ⅓ cup of the bean mixture down the center. Fold one side of the leaf just past the center, so the filling is covered. Fold the other side of the leaf to overlap the first side. Repeat, using all of the bean mixture, making a total of 8 bundles. (Save any extra lettuce for a salad.)

PER SERVING (2 BUNDLES): 166 Cal, 4 g Fat, 0 g Sat Fat, 0 g Trans Fat, 0 mg Chol, 322 mg Sod, 29 g Carb, 4 g Fib, 11 g Prot, 47 mg Calc. *POINTS* value: *3.*

★

★ **tip** If you're in a time-crunch, simply spoon the bean mixture into lettuce cups, as pictured.

MAKES 4 SERVINGS

1 (19-ounce) can **black beans**, rinsed and drained

½ cup **corn kernels**

½ **red bell pepper**, seeded and chopped

4 **scallions**, sliced

¼ cup chopped **fresh cilantro**

2 tablespoons **fresh lime juice**

2 teaspoons **olive oil**

1 teaspoon ground **cumin**

1 **garlic clove**, chopped

½ teaspoon **salt**

1 head **Boston lettuce**, cleaned and separated into leaves

Corn and Black-Bean
Lettuce Bundles

Tomatoes Stuffed with Herbed Couscous

Tomatoes Stuffed with Herbed Couscous

This recipe is best made in the summer, when local tomatoes are at their peak. Try other grains for the stuffing, like brown rice, bulgur, or barley.

1. Combine the water, tomato paste, and oil in a medium saucepan; bring to a boil. Stir in the couscous, lemon juice, parsley, basil, cinnamon, salt, and pepper. Remove from the heat; cover and let stand until the liquid is absorbed, about 5 minutes. Uncover, gently fluff the couscous with a fork, transfer to a bowl and let cool completely.

2. Meanwhile, cut off the top half inch of each tomato, reserving the slices to use as lids. Scoop out the seeds and membranes. Fill the tomatoes with the couscous and top with the lids.

PER SERVING (1 STUFFED TOMATO): 182 Cal, 2 g Fat, 0 g Sat Fat, 0 g Trans Fat, 0 mg Chol, 161 mg Sod, 37 g Carb, 6 g Fib, 7 g Prot, 28 mg Calc. *POINTS* value: *3.*

MAKES 8 SERVINGS

1 ½ cups **water**

1 tablespoon **tomato paste**

2 teaspoons **olive oil**

1 ½ cups **whole-wheat couscous**

¼ cup **fresh lemon juice**

2 tablespoons chopped **fresh parsley**

1 teaspoon **dried basil**, crumbled

½ teaspoon **cinnamon**

½ teaspoon **salt**

⅛ teaspoon freshly **ground pepper**

8 **tomatoes**

Grilled Portobello Mushrooms on Greens

Meaty Portobello mushrooms are marinated briefly in a balsamic-thyme vinaigrette, charred on the grill, then sliced while still warm and arranged atop greens.

1. Spray the grill or broiler rack with olive oil nonstick spray; prepare the grill or preheat the broiler.

2. Combine the vinegar, oil, soy sauce, and thyme in a shallow dish. Add the mushrooms and let stand, turning frequently, about 10 minutes.

3. Grill or broil the mushrooms 5 inches from the heat, brushing with any remaining marinade, until heated through, 1–2 minutes on each side. Slice thinly and serve at once over the greens.

PER SERVING (1 MUSHROOM WITH ABOUT 1 CUP GREENS): 60 Cal, 3 g Fat, 0 g Sat Fat, 0 g Trans Fat, 0 mg Chol, 174 mg Sod, 7 g Carb, 3 g Fib, 3 g Prot, 39 mg Calc. **POINTS** value: *1*

MAKES 4 SERVINGS

- 1 tablespoon **balsamic** or **red-wine vinegar**
- 2 teaspoons **extra-virgin olive oil**
- 2 teaspoons reduced-sodium **soy sauce**
- 1 teaspoon minced **fresh thyme**
- 4 fresh **Portobello mushrooms**, stems discarded
- 4 cups mesclun or mixed **salad greens**

CHAPTER 2

Just Soups

Beef, Mushroom, and Barley Soup

This "throw it in the pot and forget it" soup features chunks of lean round steak, pearl barley, and plenty of veggies. If you like, add some chopped fresh herbs—like thyme or marjoram—with the lima beans and mushrooms in step 2, but the soup will be just as delicious without further embellishment.

1. Combine the beef, barley, and water in a large saucepan; bring to a boil. Skim off any foam, then add the carrots, onions, celery, salt, fennel seeds (if using), and pepper; return to a boil. Reduce the heat and simmer, covered, 45 minutes.

2. Stir in the lima beans and mushrooms; simmer, covered, until the beef is fork-tender, about 15 minutes longer.

PER SERVING (about 2 cups): 301 Cal, 6 g Fat, 2 g Sat Fat, 1 g Trans Fat, 43 mg Chol, 666 mg Sod, 39 g Carb, 9 g Fib, 24 g Prot, 55 mg Calc. **POINTS** value: **6.**

★

★ **tip** If you want to intensify the flavor of the soup and give it a rich, dark color, spray the saucepan with canola oil nonstick spray before you add the barley and water in step 1, and brown the beef in batches. You can also toast the barley in a large dry skillet over medium-high heat, stirring constantly, until fragrant, about 5 minutes.

MAKES 6 SERVINGS 🍳

1 pound boneless lean **top round steak**, trimmed of all visible fat and cut into 1-inch chunks

¾ cup **pearl barley**

7 cups **water**

3 **carrots**, chopped

2 **onions**, chopped

3 **celery** stalks, chopped

1½ teaspoons **salt**

½ teaspoon **fennel seeds** (optional)

¼ teaspoon freshly **ground pepper**

1½ cups thawed frozen **baby lima beans**

1½ cups sliced fresh **white mushrooms**

Beef, Mushroom, and Barley Soup

Smoky Black-Bean Soup

Canadian bacon and chipotle chile pepper (smoked jalapeño pepper) give this hearty soup its wonderful smoky taste. Some of the beans are pureed to thicken the soup, but if you like your soup a little thicker, add more beans to the blender. Garnish each serving with a sprinkling of finely chopped onion if you like.

1. Place 2 cans of the black beans in a colander; rinse and drain. Transfer the beans to a bowl and stir in the remaining can of beans.

2. Spray a large saucepan with canola oil nonstick spray and set over medium-high heat. Add the bacon and cook, stirring occasionally, until browned, 3–4 minutes. Add the onion, bell peppers, and garlic; cook, stirring occasionally, until the vegetables are softened and lightly browned, 6–7 minutes. Add the cumin and chile pepper; cook, stirring constantly, until fragrant, about 30 seconds. Add the beans and broth; bring to a boil. Reduce the heat and simmer until slightly thickened, about 30 minutes.

3. Remove the saucepan from the heat; let cool about 10 minutes. Pour 4 cups of the soup into a blender or food processor and puree. Return the pureed soup to the saucepan and stir in the salt. Cook, stirring occasionally, over medium-high heat until heated through, about 2 minutes.

PER SERVING (1⅓ cups): 209 Cal, 3 g Fat, 0 g Sat Fat, 0 g Trans Fat, 9 mg Chol, 1,195 mg Sod, 29 g Carb, 11 g Fib, 16 g Prot, 69 mg Calc. **POINTS** value: **4.**

MAKES 6 SERVINGS

3 (15½-ounce) cans **black beans**

¼ pound **Canadian bacon,** trimmed of all visible fat and chopped

1 **onion,** chopped

1 **green bell pepper,** seeded and chopped

1 **red bell pepper,** seeded and chopped

3 **garlic cloves,** minced

1 teaspoon ground **cumin**

½ teaspoon ground **chipotle chile pepper**

4 cups reduced-sodium **chicken broth**

¼ teaspoon **salt**

Greek Chicken, Spinach, and Rice Soup

This speedy soup gets its inspiration from *avgolemono*, a Greek lemony chicken soup usually made with rice. As with Chinese egg-drop soup, some of the hot broth is whisked into beaten egg and then returned to the soup, thickening it and creating long, delicious (and beautiful!) strands of cooked egg floating through the broth.

1. Combine the broth and chicken in a large saucepan or Dutch oven; bring to a boil. Reduce the heat and simmer until the chicken is cooked through, about 6 minutes. Remove the chicken and, when cool enough to handle, shred into bite-size pieces.

2. Meanwhile, whisk the eggs and lemon juice until frothy in a medium bowl. Gradually whisk in 1 cup of the hot broth.

3. Add the spinach to the broth remaining in the saucepan; bring to a boil. Reduce the heat to low and stir in the rice. Slowly add the egg-broth mixture, whisking constantly to avoid curdling. Continue whisking until thickened, about 3 minutes—do not allow the soup to boil. Stir in the chicken and cook until heated through. Season with the pepper and serve at once.

PER SERVING (about 1¾ cups): 242 Cal, 5 g Fat, 1 g Sat Fat, 0 g Trans Fat, 138 mg Chol, 736 mg Sod, 28 g Carb, 4 g Fib, 22 g Prot, 108 mg Calc. **POINTS** value: **4.**

★
★ **tip** You'll need ⅔ cup uncooked brown rice to get 2 cups of cooked rice.

MAKES 4 SERVINGS

4 cups reduced-sodium **chicken broth**

½ pound skinless boneless **chicken breast**, trimmed of all visible fat

2 large **eggs**

¼ cup **fresh lemon juice**

1 (10-ounce) box **frozen chopped spinach**, thawed and squeezed dry

2 cups hot cooked **brown rice**

Freshly **ground pepper** to taste

Minted Double-Pea Soup

4 POINTS VALUE

Minted Double-Pea Soup

Split-pea soup with ham is always a homey favorite. When baby peas and mint are stirred into the mix, they add a bright-green color, refreshing taste, and nice texture. If you're making the soup ahead of time, you can refrigerate it for up to 3 days or freeze it for up to 6 months, but don't add the baby peas and mint until you're ready to reheat it.

1. Combine the water, split peas, onion, carrot, garlic, salt, and pepper in a Dutch oven; bring to a boil. Reduce the heat and simmer, covered, stirring occasionally, until the split peas are soft, about 45 minutes.

2. Stir in the ham and peas. Simmer, covered, until the peas are tender, about 5 minutes. Remove the Dutch oven from the heat and stir in the mint.

PER SERVING (1 ¼ cups): 238 Cal, 2 g Fat, 1 g Sat Fat, 0 g Trans Fat, 13 mg Chol, 992 mg Sod, 38 g Carb, 14 g Fib, 19 g Prot, 56 mg Calc. *POINTS* value: *4.*

★

★ **tip** This soup is delicious topped with herbed rye croutons. To make the croutons, preheat the oven to 425°F. Spread 2 slices of rye bread, cut into ½-inch cubes, on a baking sheet. Lightly spray the bread cubes with olive oil nonstick spray, sprinkle with ¼ teaspoon dried thyme, and toss. Bake, tossing once, until golden and crisp, about 8 minutes. Let the croutons cool, then sprinkle over each serving (¼ cup croutons for each serving will increase the *POINTS* value by 1).

MAKES 4 SERVINGS 🍲

4 cups **water**

1 cup **split peas**, picked over, rinsed, and drained

1 **onion**, chopped

1 **carrot**, chopped

2 **garlic cloves**, chopped

1 teaspoon **salt**

¼ teaspoon freshly **ground pepper**

¼ pound **ham steak**, trimmed of all visible fat and diced

1 cup **frozen baby peas**

¼ cup chopped **fresh mint**

Shrimp and Soba in Fragrant Broth

Soba is a Japanese noodle made from buckwheat flour. Highly flavored with a nutty bite, it works nicely with sweet shrimp, colorful vegetables, and a ginger-infused broth. Look for soba in the Asian-foods section of most supermarkets.

1. Cook the noodles according to package directions. Drain, rinse under cold water, and set aside.

2. Combine the broth, mushrooms, ginger, garlic, scallions, carrot, and soy sauce in a large saucepan; bring to a boil over medium-high heat. Reduce the heat and simmer until the vegetables are tender, about 15 minutes. Add the shrimp and snow peas; return to a simmer. Cook until the shrimp are just opaque in the center and the snow peas are crisp-tender, 3–4 minutes.

3. Divide the noodles among 4 bowls; fill each bowl with one-quarter of the broth mixture.

PER SERVING (1½ cups broth mixture with about ⅔ cup noodles): 263 Cal, 1 g Fat, 0 g Sat Fat, 0 g Trans Fat, 126 mg Chol, 1,024 mg Sod, 41 g Carb, 3 g Fib, 27 g Prot, 53 mg Calc. *POINTS* value: *5.*

MAKES 4 SERVINGS

6 ounces **soba noodles**

4 cups reduced-sodium **chicken broth**

¼ pound sliced fresh **white mushrooms**

4 quarter-size slices peeled **fresh ginger**

3 **garlic cloves**, sliced

2 **scallions**, cut into 1-inch pieces

1 **carrot**, sliced

1 tablespoon reduced-sodium **soy sauce**

¾ pound peeled and deveined large **shrimp**

1 cup fresh **snow peas**, trimmed

Shrimp and Soba in Fragrant Broth

3 POINTS VALUE

Home-Style Chicken Soup

Simmering chicken thighs in chicken broth accomplishes two things: It enriches the flavor of the broth and it provides juicy chicken meat to add to the soup. We use chopped fresh parsley in this recipe, but you can also try chopped fresh thyme, dill, or a combination of the three.

1. Heat the oil in a large nonstick saucepan over medium heat. Add the leeks, carrot, and onion; cook, stirring occasionally, until softened, about 10 minutes. Add the chicken and broth; bring to a boil. Reduce the heat and simmer, covered, until the chicken is cooked through, about 20 minutes.

2. Transfer the chicken to a cutting board and let cool slightly. Remove the chicken from the bones and chop; return the chicken to the soup. Add the parsley, salt, and pepper. Simmer until the chicken is heated through, 2–3 minutes.

PER SERVING (about 1 cup): 137 Cal, 5 g Fat, 1 g Sat Fat, 0 g Trans Fat, 25 mg Chol, 797 mg Sod, 13 g Carb, 2 g Fib, 11 g Prot, 44 mg Calc. *POINTS* value: *3.*

MAKES 4 SERVINGS ☛

2 teaspoons **olive oil**

2 **leeks**, trimmed to white and light-green parts, cleaned, and thinly sliced

1 **carrot**, thinly sliced

1 **onion**, finely chopped

2 (¼-pound) **chicken thighs**, skinned and trimmed of all visible fat

3 cups reduced-sodium **chicken broth**

1 tablespoon chopped **fresh parsley**

½ teaspoon **salt**

¼ teaspoon freshly **ground pepper**

Wild Mushroom Soup

White and cremini mushrooms pair up in this silky, soothingly rich soup. If you want an even more pronounced mushroom flavor, soak ½ ounce dried mushrooms in warm water for 20 minutes. With a slotted spoon, transfer the mushrooms to a sieve, rinse with cold water, and then add to the fresh mushrooms in step 1.

1. Combine 3 cups of the mushrooms with 1½ cups of the broth in a medium saucepan; bring to a boil. Reduce the heat and simmer, covered, about 20 minutes. Transfer to a blender or food processor; puree, then return to the saucepan.

2. Meanwhile, spray a large nonstick saucepan with canola oil nonstick spray and set over medium heat. Add the onions, carrot, and celery; cook, stirring occasionally, until softened, about 5 minutes. Add the remaining mushrooms and cook, stirring occasionally, until the vegetables are wilted, about 10 minutes. Add the vegetable mixture to the mushroom puree in the saucepan, along with the milk and remaining 1½ cups broth; bring to a boil. Reduce the heat and simmer, stirring occasionally, about 10 minutes. Add the parsley, thyme, marjoram, and pepper; simmer 5 minutes.

PER SERVING (about 1¼ cups): 131 Cal, 1 g Fat, 0 g Sat Fat, 0 g Trans Fat, 3 mg Chol, 571 mg Sod, 23 g Carb, 3 g Fib, 12 g Prot, 232 mg Calc. **POINTS** value: **2**.

★
★ **tip** Always clean mushrooms just before using, but never immerse them in water, as they're highly absorbent and apt to become mushy. Instead, rinse them under cold running water and blot dry with paper towels. Or simply wipe them off with a damp paper towel. If you don't mind spending a little extra money, you can use 1 pound cremini mushrooms.

MAKES 4 SERVINGS

½ pound fresh **white mushrooms**, coarsely chopped

½ pound fresh **cremini mushrooms**, coarsely chopped

3 cups reduced-sodium **chicken broth**

2 **onions**, finely chopped

1 **carrot**, thinly sliced

1 **celery** stalk, finely chopped

1 cup **evaporated fat-free milk**

¼ cup finely chopped **fresh parsley**

¼ teaspoon **dried thyme**

¼ teaspoon **dried marjoram**

Freshly **ground pepper** to taste

2
POINTS
VALUE

Puree of Potato and Leek Soup

It's hard to believe that just five ingredients can create such a flavorful soup—but it's no accident when you start with buttery-tasting Yukon Gold potatoes and plenty of leeks and onion.

1. Combine all of the ingredients in a large pot; bring to a boil. Reduce the heat and simmer, covered, until the vegetables are tender, about 25 minutes. Remove from the heat and let cool about 10 minutes.

2. Pour the soup in batches into a blender or food processor and puree. Return the soup to the pot and simmer until heated through.

PER SERVING (about 1 ⅓ cups): 141 Cal, 0 g Fat, 0 g Sat Fat, 0 g Trans Fat, 0 mg Chol, 551 mg Sod, 32 g Carb, 3 g Fib, 4 g Prot, 49 mg Calc. *POINTS* value: *2.*

★ **tip** To clean leeks thoroughly, cut off the roots and dark-green tops. Cut the leeks in half and rinse under cool running water, separating the sections and rubbing them to remove all the sand. Sometimes leeks come in various sizes; you'll need about 2½ pounds for this recipe. Garnish the soup with 2 tablespoons of snipped fresh chives if you like.

MAKES 6 SERVINGS

- 4 **Yukon Gold potatoes**, peeled and cut into ½-inch pieces

- 4 large **leeks**, trimmed to white and light-green parts, cleaned, and chopped

- 1 large **onion**, chopped

- 5 cups reduced-sodium **chicken broth**

- ¼ teaspoon freshly **ground pepper**

Hot and Sour Soup

Hot-and-sour soup provides the perfect balance of heat and tang. Dried shiitake mushrooms give the brew a rich, woodsy flavor; the tofu and bamboo shoots are pleasantly mild and toothsome. Look for dried shiitakes in the produce section of the supermarket or in Asian markets.

1. Combine the mushrooms with enough hot water to cover by 1 inch in a large bowl. Let stand 15 minutes. Drain and slice the mushrooms.

2. Meanwhile, combine the egg and egg white in a small bowl; beat lightly.

3. Combine the mushrooms, broth, tofu, bamboo shoots, soy sauce, vinegar, and hot pepper sauce in a large saucepan; bring to a boil. Reduce the heat; simmer until the mushrooms are tender and the flavors are blended, about 15 minutes.

4. Return the soup to a boil. Slowly drizzle the egg mixture into the soup while stirring in a circular motion; cook 1 minute. Remove the saucepan from the heat and stir in the scallions.

PER SERVING (1¼ cups): 131 Cal, 4 g Fat, 0 g Sat Fat, 0 g Trans Fat, 53 mg Chol, 1,003 mg Sod, 12 g Carb, 3 g Fib, 13 g Prot, 43 mg Calc. *POINTS* value: *2.*

MAKES 4 SERVINGS

- 8 **dried shiitake mushrooms**
- 1 large **egg**
- 1 **egg white**
- 3 cups reduced-sodium **chicken broth**
- 8 ounces reduced-fat firm **tofu**, drained and cut into ¼-inch cubes
- 1 (8-ounce) can sliced **bamboo shoots**, drained
- 3 tablespoons reduced-sodium **soy sauce**
- 3 tablespoons **rice vinegar**
- 1½ teaspoons **hot pepper sauce**
- 3 **scallions**, chopped

Roasted Garlic, Red Pepper,
and Potato Soup

2 POINTS VALUE

Roasted Garlic, Red Pepper, and Potato Soup

This wonderful winter warmer contains the kind of simple ingredients you might well have in your pantry. Although the soup won't freeze well—because potato purees tend to break down in a freezer—it will keep in the refrigerator for up to 4 days.

1. Preheat the oven to 425°F. Cut the top third off the garlic bulb and discard. Wrap the garlic in foil and bake until soft, about 45 minutes. Let cool.

2. Meanwhile, combine the broth, potatoes, onion, celery, carrot, salt, and pepper in a Dutch oven; bring to a boil. Reduce the heat and simmer, covered, until the vegetables are tender, about 20 minutes. Remove from the heat and let cool slightly.

3. Puree the roasted peppers in a blender. Transfer to a small bowl and set aside.

4. Squeeze the garlic pulp into a clean blender or food processor. Add the broth-and-vegetable mixture in batches to the blender, and puree. Stir in the thyme. Serve with the roasted-pepper puree.

PER SERVING (1 cup soup with 2 tablespoons roasted-pepper puree): 120 Cal, 0 g Fat, 0 g Sat Fat, 0 g Trans Fat, 0 mg Chol, 549 mg Sod, 27 g Carb, 3 g Fib, 4 g Prot, 46 mg Calc. *POINTS* value: *2*.

★
★ **tip** You can serve this elegant soup in two ways: Either drizzle the roasted-pepper puree onto each serving and swirl gently with a spoon for a marble effect, or stir it in completely for a beautiful crimson-colored soup.

MAKES 4 SERVINGS

1 **garlic bulb**

2 cups reduced-sodium **chicken broth**

2 **Yukon Gold potatoes**, peeled and diced (about 2 cups)

1 large **onion**, chopped

1 **celery** stalk, chopped

1 large **carrot**, chopped

¼ teaspoon **salt**

⅛ teaspoon freshly **ground pepper**

1 (7-ounce) jar **roasted red peppers**, drained

2 teaspoons chopped **fresh thyme**

Lentil Soup with Caraway

Caraway seeds lend a nutty, delicate, anise flavor to this soothing lentil and vegetable soup. Try stirring in a couple of teaspoons of balsamic vinegar just before serving to give it extra sparkle and zing.

1. Heat the oil in a Dutch oven over medium heat. Add the leeks and cook, stirring occasionally, until softened, about 10 minutes. Add the caraway seeds and allspice and cook, stirring constantly, until fragrant, about 1 minute. Stir in the broth, potato, parsnips, and lentils; bring to a boil. Reduce the heat and simmer, stirring occasionally, until the vegetables and lentils are softened, about 20 minutes. Stir in the salt and pepper.

2. Meanwhile, combine ¼ cup of the parsley and the radishes in a small bowl.

3. Remove the soup from the heat; stir in the remaining ½ cup parsley and the spinach. Garnish each serving with the parsley-radish mixture.

PER SERVING (about 1⅓ cups soup with about 2 tablespoons radish mixture): 260 Cal, 3 g Fat, 0 g Sat Fat, 0 g Trans Fat, 0 mg Chol, 839 mg Sod, 46 g Carb, 12 g Fib, 15 g Prot, 81 mg Calc. *POINTS* value: **5.**

★

★ **tip** Double this recipe (using an 8-quart Dutch oven) to make a really large batch. It'll take about the same amount of time, and you can freeze half the soup for almost-instant meals later. Chicken broth may be substituted for the vegetable broth.

MAKES 6 SERVINGS

- 1 tablespoon **olive oil**
- 2 **leeks**, trimmed to white and light-green parts, cleaned, halved lengthwise, and thinly sliced
- ¾ teaspoon **caraway seeds**, crushed
- ½ teaspoon ground **allspice**
- 6 cups reduced-sodium **vegetable broth**
- 1 large (½-pound) **sweet potato**, peeled and chopped
- 2 **parsnips**, peeled, quartered lengthwise, and thinly sliced
- ½ pound **lentils**, picked over, rinsed, and drained
- ½ teaspoon **salt**
- ¼ teaspoon freshly **ground pepper**
- ¾ cup finely chopped flat-leaf **parsley**
- 6 **radishes**, thinly sliced
- 1 small bunch **spinach**, cleaned, stems discarded, and leaves roughly chopped

1 POINTS VALUE

Ginger-Lemon Borscht

Fresh ginger, lemon juice, and lemon zest give this classic beet soup a wonderful bracing flavor. Use a food processor for shredding the vegetables and you'll have the soup ready in no time flat.

Combine the broth, beets, carrot, parsnip, cabbage, scallions, lemon juice, ginger, lemon zest, salt, and pepper in a Dutch oven; bring to a boil. Reduce the heat and simmer until the vegetables are just tender, about 15 minutes. Garnish each serving with the yogurt and cilantro.

PER SERVING (about 2 cups soup with 2 tablespoons yogurt and 1 tablespoon cilantro): 113 Cal, 0 g Fat, 0 g Sat Fat, 0 g Trans Fat, 1 mg Chol, 1,008 mg Sod, 23 g Carb, 5 g Fib, 7 g Prot, 86 mg Calc. *POINTS* value: *1*.

★

★ **tip** You'll need 4 medium beets for this recipe. To keep your hands from becoming stained when handling the beets, wear disposable plastic gloves (available at drugstores).

MAKES 4 SERVINGS 🍲

- 5 cups reduced-sodium **chicken broth**
- 2 cups shredded peeled fresh **beets**
- 1 **carrot**, shredded
- 1 **parsnip**, peeled and shredded
- 1 cup finely shredded **red cabbage**
- 3 large **scallions**, thinly sliced
- 2 tablespoons **fresh lemon juice**
- 2 teaspoons minced peeled **fresh ginger**
- ½ teaspoon grated **lemon zest**
- ¼ teaspoon **salt**
- ¼ teaspoon freshly **ground pepper**
- ½ cup plain **fat-free yogurt**
- ¼ cup **fresh cilantro** leaves, for garnish

Pineapple Gazpacho

Crushed pineapple provides a sweet note to this unusual and delightful interpretation of the classic tomato soup from Spain. It's perfect to serve ice cold on a hot summer's day. If you like, garnish each serving with fresh pineapple wedges.

Combine all of the ingredients in a large bowl. Refrigerate, covered, until very cold, at least 3 hours or overnight.

PER SERVING (about 1⅓ cups): 106 Cal, 1 g Fat, 0 g Sat Fat, 0 g Trans Fat, 0 mg Chol, 706 mg Sod, 23 g Carb, 5 g Fib, 5 g Prot, 59 mg Calc. *POINTS* value: *1*.

MAKES 6 SERVINGS

1 (28- or 35-ounce) can **crushed tomatoes**

3 cups reduced-sodium **chicken broth**

1 (20-ounce) can **crushed pineapple** in juice, drained

1 seedless **cucumber**, chopped

1 small **red onion**, finely chopped

1 **celery** stalk, chopped

½ **red bell pepper**, seeded and chopped

½ **yellow bell pepper**, seeded and chopped

½ cup chopped **fresh cilantro**

1 **garlic clove**, minced

½ to 1 **jalapeño pepper**, seeded and chopped

1 teaspoon ground **cumin**

½ teaspoon **hot pepper sauce**

½ teaspoon **coriander**

½ teaspoon **salt**

¼ teaspoon **chili powder**

¼ teaspoon freshly **ground pepper**

Broccoli-Cheese Soup

Cheese and broccoli have always been a winning combination, and this luscious soup proves it doesn't need to be off-limits if you're trying to eat healthfully. Because food processors weren't designed to handle a lot of liquid, they tend to leak when you puree soups. Unless your food processor is very large, using a blender for this recipe is a smarter—and neater—idea.

1. Combine the broccoli and broth in a large saucepan; bring to a boil. Reduce the heat and simmer until the broccoli is tender, about 10 minutes.

2. Transfer the broccoli and about ½ cup of the cooking liquid to a blender. Puree until very smooth, scraping the sides of the blender every 30 seconds. Remove the knob from the lid and with the machine running, gradually pour the remaining liquid through the hole. Place a large sieve over the saucepan and strain the soup back into the saucepan. Stir in the milk, salt, and pepper; simmer until heated through, about 5 minutes. Remove the saucepan from the heat, add the cheese, and stir until melted.

PER SERVING (about 1¼ cups): 58 Cal, 1 g Fat, 0 g Sat Fat, 0 g Trans Fat, 3 mg Chol, 1,078 mg Sod, 7 g Carb, 2 g Fib, 8 g Prot, 179 mg Calc. *POINTS* value: *1.*

★

★ **tip** Serve with whole-wheat toast for a satisfying supper (1 slice with each serving will increase the *POINTS* value by 2).

MAKES 4 SERVINGS

4 cups **broccoli** florets

2½ cups **vegetable broth**

¼ cup **fat-free milk**

½ teaspoon **salt**

¼ teaspoon freshly ground **pepper**

½ cup shredded **fat-free sharp cheddar cheese**

Cajun Tomato Soup

This zesty soup gets its taste of the bayou from the Cajun seasoning—a blend of cayenne, paprika, garlic, and onion—and hot pepper sauce. If you're looking to fix something fancy, add ½ pound chopped peeled and deveined shrimp to the finished soup and simmer until the shrimp are just opaque in the center, about 2 minutes.

Spray a large nonstick saucepan with canola oil nonstick spray and set over medium-high heat. Add the onion and cook, stirring occasionally, until softened, about 5 minutes. Add the tomatoes, broth, and tomato paste; bring to a boil. Reduce the heat and simmer, covered, 15 minutes. Transfer to a blender and puree. Return to the saucepan and stir in the corn, milk, seasoning, pepper, and pepper sauce. Simmer until the soup is heated through.

PER SERVING (about 1¼ cups): 114 Cal, 1 g Fat, 0 g Sat Fat, 0 g Trans Fat, 1 mg Chol, 442 mg Sod, 25 g Carb, 4 g Fib, 6 g Prot, 117 mg Calc. *POINTS* value: *2.*

MAKES 4 SERVINGS

- 1 **onion**, chopped
- 1 (14½-ounce) can diced **tomatoes**
- 1½ cups reduced-sodium **vegetable broth**
- 2 tablespoons **tomato paste**
- 1 cup thawed frozen **corn kernels**
- 1 cup **fat-free milk**
- ½ teaspoon **Cajun seasoning**
- ¼ teaspoon freshly **ground pepper**
- ¼ teaspoon **hot pepper sauce**

CHAPTER 3
Main-Dish Salads and Side Salads

Grilled Thai Beef Salad

Grilled Thai Beef Salad

Thai salads often call for sugar to balance the acidity in their dressings. For this rendition of Thai beef salad, we use the natural sweetness of finely minced carrots to mellow the lime juice and soy sauce.

1. Spray a grill rack with canola oil nonstick spray; prepare the grill.

2. Lightly spray the steak with canola oil nonstick spray and sprinkle with the salt. Grill the steak 5 inches from the heat until an instant-read thermometer inserted in the center of the steak registers 145°F for medium-rare, 3–4 minutes on each side. Transfer the steak to a cutting board and let stand 5 minutes. Slice thinly on an angle across the grain.

3. Meanwhile, put ¼ cup of the carrots, the soy sauce, water, lime juice, ginger, and chile in a mini-food processor; process until the carrots and chile are very finely minced. Transfer to a large bowl. Add the remaining 1 cup carrots, the steak, lettuce, cucumber, bell pepper, mint, and onion; mix well.

PER SERVING (2 CUPS): 183 Cal, 7 g Fat, 3 g Sat Fat, 1 g Trans Fat, 41 mg Chol, 672 mg Sod, 12 g Carb, 5 g Fib, 20 g Prot, 70 mg Calc. *POINTS* value: *3.*

★
★ **tip** Nuts are a traditional garnish in many Thai dishes—sprinkle this salad with 20 chopped peanuts and you'll increase the per-serving *POINTS* value by ½.

MAKES 4 SERVINGS 🔥 🕐

1 (¾-pound) lean **flank steak**, trimmed of all visible fat

¼ teaspoon **salt**

1 ¼ cups shredded **carrots**

3 tablespoons reduced-sodium **soy sauce**

3 tablespoons **water**

3 tablespoons **fresh lime juice**

1 tablespoon minced peeled **fresh ginger**

1 **serrano chile**, seeded and coarsely chopped (wear gloves to prevent irritation)

3 cups shredded **romaine lettuce**

½ seedless **cucumber**, halved lengthwise and thinly sliced

1 **red bell pepper**, seeded and thinly sliced

¾ cup coarsely chopped **fresh mint**

½ cup thinly sliced **red onion**

Curried Chicken Salad with Grapes

Choose red or green seedless grapes for this salad, whichever tastes sweeter, to balance the tanginess of the yogurt and curry dressing.

1. Combine the chicken, grapes, carrot, celery, parsley, and lemon juice in a medium bowl.

2. Combine the onion, yogurt, curry powder, salt, and pepper in a small bowl. Pour over the chicken mixture and toss to combine. Divide the mesclun among 4 salad plates and top with the chicken salad.

PER SERVING (1 CUP GREENS AND ABOUT 1 CUP CHICKEN SALAD): 171 Cal, 4 g Fat, 1 g Sat Fat, 0 g Trans Fat, 60 mg Chol, 349 mg Sod, 11 g Carb, 2 g Fib, 24 g Prot, 95 mg Calc. *POINTS* value: *3*.

★

★ **tip** Sprinkle each salad with a half dozen toasted almonds and up the per-serving *POINTS* value by 1.

MAKES 4 SERVINGS ✱ 🕐

2 cups shredded cooked skinless **chicken breast**

20 small **seedless grapes**, halved

1 **carrot**, coarsely grated

½ **celery** stalk, thinly sliced

1 tablespoon chopped **fresh parsley**

1 tablespoon **fresh lemon juice**

½ **onion**, grated

¼ cup plain **fat-free yogurt**

1 teaspoon **curry powder**

½ teaspoon **salt**

¼ teaspoon freshly **ground pepper**

4 cups mesclun **salad greens**

Mediterranean Salad with Feta

Dishes like this one are meant to be prepared in the summer when tomatoes are at their peak. If plum tomatoes look best, you'll need to use 6 of them. This salad is required to stand at room temperature before serving to allow the flavors to blend, but it should not stand for more than 1 hour.

Combine all of the ingredients in a large bowl. Let stand at room temperature, covered, at least 30 minutes or up to 1 hour.

PER SERVING (ABOUT 1 CUP): 110 Cal, 3 g Fat, 1 g Sat Fat, 0 g Trans Fat, 0 mg Chol, 595 mg Sod, 17 g Carb, 3 g Fib, 7 g Prot, 112 mg Calc. *POINTS* value: *2.*

★

★ **tip** Crunchy, juicy Kirby cucumbers are usually used for pickling, but their light, sweet flavor makes them a pleasant addition to salads as well. Their skins are not waxed, so peeling is unnecessary.

MAKES 4 SERVINGS

- 4 **tomatoes**, chopped
- 4 Kirby **cucumbers**, chopped
- 2 **yellow bell peppers**, seeded and chopped
- 3 ounces **fat-free feta cheese**, crumbled
- 1 tablespoon **fresh lemon juice**
- 2 teaspoons **olive oil**
- ½ teaspoon kosher **salt**

Fennel Salad with Mint, Olives, and Turkey

Not only is this salad a truly fabulous combination of flavors, but it also has a great mix of textures — and it's gorgeous. In addition, you get lean turkey, lots of vegetables, and good-for-you spinach all in one bowl.

1. Combine the fennel, fennel fronds, onion, mint, 2 tablespoons of the lemon juice, the olives, oil, lemon zest, ⅛ teaspoon of the salt, and ⅛ teaspoon of the pepper in a medium bowl.

2. Combine the spinach, the remaining 1 tablespoon lemon juice, ⅛ teaspoon salt, and ⅛ teaspoon pepper in a large bowl.

3. Divide the spinach among 4 salad plates. Top each serving with one-quarter of the fennel salad, and arrange one-quarter of the turkey on the side.

PER SERVING (2 CUPS SPINACH WITH 1 CUP FENNEL SALAD AND ½ CUP TURKEY): 181 Cal, 6 g Fat, 1 g Sat Fat, 0 g Trans Fat, 21 mg Chol, 855 mg Sod, 23 g Carb, 8 g Fib, 13 g Prot, 122 mg Calc. *POINTS* value: *3.*

★

★ **tip** For a more stylized presentation, prepare the spinach as directed in step 2 and arrange on a large serving platter. Top with separate rows of the fennel and fennel fronds, onion, olives, and turkey. Combine the mint, 2 tablespoons of the lemon juice, the oil, lemon zest, ⅛ teaspoon of the salt, and ⅛ teaspoon of the pepper in a bowl; drizzle over the salad.

MAKES 4 SERVINGS 🕏 🕐

2 large **fennel bulbs,** cut into matchstick-thin strips

1 tablespoon finely chopped **fennel fronds**

¾ cup finely chopped **red onion**

⅓ cup coarsely chopped **fresh mint**

3 tablespoons **fresh lemon juice**

2 tablespoons chopped brine-cured **green olives**

1 tablespoon **olive oil**

2 teaspoons grated **lemon zest**

¼ teaspoon **salt**

¼ teaspoon freshly **ground pepper**

8 cups baby **spinach**

2 cups thin strips cooked skinless **turkey breast**

Fennel Salad with Mint, Olives, and Turkey

Green Goddess Garden Salad

Green Goddess Garden Salad

Invented in the 1920s at San Francisco's Palace Hotel, Green Goddess dressing has become a staple in the lore of American salads. Our version, with tangy fat-free yogurt, contains all the traditional fresh herbs that give the dressing its vibrant green color and bracing taste.

1. To prepare the dressing, puree the yogurt, chives, dill, scallion, mint, salt, and pepper in a blender or food processor.

2. To prepare the salad, combine the spinach, romaine, watercress, snow peas, cucumber, carrot, and bell pepper in a large bowl. Add the dressing and toss to combine. Serve at once.

PER SERVING (ABOUT 2 CUPS): 98 Cal, 1 g Fat, 0 g Sat Fat, 0 g Trans Fat, 1 mg Chol, 418 mg Sod, 17 g Carb, 7 g Fib, 9 g Prot, 263 mg Calc. **POINTS** value: *1*.

★

★ **tip** Double the amount of dressing and refrigerate half for up to 3 days to use for a chicken or seafood salad later in the week.

MAKES 4 SERVINGS 🥕

¾ cup plain **fat-free yogurt**

¼ cup snipped **fresh chives**

2 tablespoons chopped **fresh dill**

1 **scallion**, thinly sliced

1 teaspoon chopped **fresh mint**

½ teaspoon **salt**

¼ teaspoon freshly **ground pepper**

1 bunch **spinach**, cleaned and torn

1 head **romaine lettuce**, cleaned and torn

1 bunch **watercress**, cleaned and stemmed

1 cup fresh **snow peas**, trimmed

1 **cucumber**, seeded and thinly sliced

1 **carrot**, grated

1 **red bell pepper**, seeded and diced

Pasta Salad with Creamy Chive Dressing

This refreshing lemony salad is just the cooling antidote to a hot summer evening. We use fusilli pasta because its curves and grooves catch every bit of the delicious dressing.

1. Combine the yogurt, chives, lemon juice, lemon zest, salt, and pepper in a small bowl. Refrigerate, covered, until the flavors are blended, at least 1 hour.

2. Cook the fusilli according to package directions adding the squash to the pot during the last minute of cooking. Drain the fusilli and squash and rinse under cold water. Place in a large serving bowl; add the bell pepper and tomatoes. Whisk the yogurt dressing, pour over the pasta mixture, and toss to coat. Garnish with the basil leaves.

PER SERVING (ABOUT 1 ¼ CUPS): 210 Cal, 1 g Fat, 0 g Sat Fat, 0 g Trans Fat, 0 mg Chol, 303 mg Sod, 46 g Carb, 6 g Fib, 9 g Prot, 46 mg Calc. **POINTS** value: **3.**

★

★ **tip** Transform this recipe into a main-dish salad by garnishing each serving with ½ cup diced cooked skinless chicken breast. (You'll increase the per-serving **POINTS** value by 2.)

MAKES 4 SERVINGS

- 2 tablespoons plain **fat-free yogurt**

- 1 teaspoon snipped **fresh chives**

- 1 teaspoon **fresh lemon juice**

- ½ teaspoon grated **lemon zest**

- ½ teaspoon **salt**

- ¼ teaspoon freshly **ground pepper**

- 2 cups **whole-wheat fusilli**

- 1 medium **yellow squash,** sliced

- 1 **red bell pepper,** seeded and diced

- 6 **cherry tomatoes,** halved

- 8 **fresh basil** leaves, thinly sliced

Creamy Vegetable Slaw

Coleslaw just got all dressed up! Savoy cabbage, radicchio, and jicama, stand in for the usual green cabbage and carrot. We lighten up the traditional mayonnaise-laden dressing with yogurt and give it plenty of zing by adding cider vinegar and grated lemon (or lime) zest.

1. Combine the cabbage, radicchio, jicama, bell pepper, and celery in a large bowl.

2. Combine the yogurt, mayonnaise, vinegar, lemon zest, salt, and pepper in a small bowl. Pour the yogurt mixture over the vegetables and toss to coat. Refrigerate, covered, until the flavors are blended, at least 1 hour.

PER SERVING (GENEROUS 1 CUP): 40 Cal, 0 g Fat, 0 g Sat Fat, 0 g Trans Fat, 0 mg Chol, 232 mg Sod, 9 g Carb, 3 g Fib, 2 g Prot, 40 mg Calc. *POINTS* value: *0*.

★
★ **tip** Jicama, a knobby root vegetable frequently used in Mexican dishes, is sweet and crunchy; its texture is similar to that of water chestnuts. Look for jicama in most supermarkets and Hispanic groceries. Steer clear of large jicamas—they tend to be dry and tough.

MAKES 8 SERVINGS

4 cups shredded **Savoy** or **green cabbage**

2 cups shredded **radicchio** or **red cabbage**

2 cups matchstick-thin strips **jicama**

1 **yellow bell pepper**, seeded and thinly sliced

2 **celery** stalks, thinly sliced

¼ cup plain **fat-free yogurt**

¼ cup **fat-free mayonnaise**

2 tablespoons **cider vinegar**

1 teaspoon grated **lemon** or **lime zest**

½ teaspoon **salt**

½ teaspoon freshly **ground pepper**

Moroccan Vegetable Salad

Crunchy veggies—tomatoes, bell peppers, and cucumbers—are topped with a garlicky chickpea puree to make a lunch straight from the casbah.

1. Combine the tomatoes, bell peppers, cucumbers, 2 tablespoons of the lemon juice, the salt, and pepper in a medium bowl. Refrigerate, covered, until the flavors are blended, about 30 minutes.

2. Meanwhile, heat the oil in a small nonstick skillet over medium heat. Add the garlic and cook, stirring constantly, until fragrant, about 30 seconds. Add the cumin and toast, stirring constantly, about 1 minute.

3. Puree the chickpeas, sour cream, and remaining 2 tablespoons lemon juice in a food processor or blender; add the garlic mixture; pulse until combined.

4. Divide the tomato mixture among 4 salad plates. Top evenly with the chickpea puree.

PER SERVING (ABOUT 1 CUP SALAD WITH ABOUT ⅓ CUP CHICKPEA PUREE): 138 Cal, 4 g Fat, 0 g Sat Fat, 0 g Trans Fat, 0 mg Chol, 289 mg Sod, 23 g Carb, 5 g Fib, 6 g Prot, 71 mg Calc. **POINTS** value: **2.**

★

★ **tip** This is an excellent salad paired with whole-wheat pita wedges. (One small pita will increase the per serving **POINTS** value by 1.)

MAKES 4 SERVINGS 🥕

- 2 large **tomatoes**, cut into wedges
- 2 **red bell peppers**, seeded and diced
- 2 Kirby **cucumbers**, diced
- 4 tablespoons **fresh lemon juice**
- ¼ teaspoon kosher **salt**
- ⅛ teaspoon freshly **ground pepper**
- 2 teaspoons **olive oil**
- 1 **garlic clove**, minced
- ¼ teaspoon ground **cumin**
- 1 cup canned **chickpeas**, rinsed and drained
- ⅓ cup **fat-free sour cream** or plain **fat-free yogurt**

Moroccan Vegetable Salad

Classic Three-Bean Salad

While many variations of bean salad abound, this recipe sticks to the basics. The combination of red- and white-wine vinegar in this salad gives it a pleasant zing.

Combine the vinegars, basil, and oil in a large bowl. Add the tomatoes, red kidney beans, cannellini beans, green beans, scallions, salt, and pepper; toss to coat. Refrigerate, covered, until chilled, about 2 hours.

PER SERVING (ABOUT 1 CUP): 156 Cal, 4 g Fat, 1 g Sat Fat, 0 g Trans Fat, 0 mg Chol, 575 mg Sod, 24 g Carb, 8 g Fib, 8 g Prot, 55 mg Calc. *POINTS* value: *3.*

MAKES 4 SERVINGS

- 2 tablespoons **white-wine vinegar**
- 1 tablespoon **red-wine vinegar**
- 1 tablespoon chopped **fresh basil**
- 1 tablespoon **olive oil**
- 2 **tomatoes**, chopped
- 1 cup canned **red kidney beans**, rinsed and drained
- 1 cup canned **cannellini (white kidney) beans**, rinsed and drained
- ⅔ cup (2-inch lengths) trimmed fresh **green beans**, steamed
- 4 **scallions**, sliced
- ¼ teaspoon **salt**
- ¼ teaspoon freshly **ground pepper**

Southwest Corn and Black-Bean Salad

This simple salad is great served with practically anything off the grill. If you have the grill going and fresh corn is in season, cook 2 ears to give you the 1 cup of corn kernels for this recipe, and add them to the salad at the last minute.

Combine all of the ingredients in a large bowl. Refrigerate, covered, until chilled, at least 2 hours.

PER SERVING (ABOUT ½ CUP SALAD): 130 Cal, 1 g Fat, 0 g Sat Fat, 0 g Trans Fat, 0 mg Chol, 180 mg Sod, 24 g Carb, 7 g Fib, 7 g Prot, 54 mg Calc. *POINTS* value: *2.*

MAKES 4 SERVINGS

- 1 (19-ounce) can **black beans**, rinsed and drained
- 1 cup fresh or thawed frozen **corn kernels**
- 8 **scallions**, sliced
- ½ cup diced **tomato**
- 2 teaspoons **fresh lime juice**
- 1 teaspoon ground **cumin**

Peppery Bean Salad

Peppery Bean Salad

Perfect for a potluck or picnic, this summery salad is studded with crunchy veggies and spiced with peppercorn ranch dressing and cracked black pepper.

Combine all of the ingredients in a large bowl. Refrigerate, covered, until the flavors are blended, at least 1 hour.

PER SERVING (ABOUT 1 CUP): 166 Cal, 1 g Fat, 0 g Sat Fat, 0 g Trans Fat, 0 mg Chol, 353 mg Sod, 32 g Carb, 10 g Fib, 9 g Prot, 57 mg Calc. *POINTS* value: **3.**

★

★ **tip** Add one slice of hearty whole-wheat bread and you'll increase the per serving *POINTS* value by 2.

MAKES 6 SERVINGS

1 cup thawed frozen **lima beans**

1 cup canned **red kidney beans**, rinsed and drained

1 cup canned **chickpeas**, rinsed and drained

1 cup canned **black beans**, rinsed and drained

1 **celery** stalk, sliced diagonally

1 **red bell pepper**, seeded and diced

½ **red onion**, finely chopped

¼ cup **fat-free creamy peppercorn ranch salad dressing**

¼ teaspoon cracked **black pepper**

Italian Fennel and White-Bean Salad

Fresh fennel, sometimes called sweet anise, has a sweet, delicate flavor. When selecting fennel, choose fairly large, squat bulbs with a pearly sheen and no sign of splitting, drying, or browning. Serve this salad with just about anything Italian or with pork.

Combine the vinegar, oil, salt, sage, and pepper in a large bowl. Add the fennel and beans; toss to coat.

PER SERVING (ABOUT ½ CUP): 87 Cal, 2 g Fat, 0 g Sat Fat, 0 g Trans Fat, 0 mg Chol, 389 mg Sod, 14 g Carb, 4 g Fib, 3 g Prot, 51 mg Calc. *POINTS* value: *1.*

★ **tip** If the stalks are attached to the fennel bulb, they should sport fluffy green fronds. Don't discard these delicate fennel leaves—they add a delightful hint of anise flavor and can be chopped and added to salads, soups, and pasta dishes.

MAKES 8 SERVINGS

2 tablespoons **balsamic vinegar**

1 tablespoon **olive oil**

¾ teaspoon **salt**

½ teaspoon **dried sage**, crumbled

¼ teaspoon freshly **ground pepper**

2 **fennel bulbs**, thinly sliced

1 (19-ounce) can **cannellini (white kidney) beans**, rinsed and drained

Tricolor Pepper and Penne Salad

Green, red, and yellow bell peppers do a quick toss with nutty whole-wheat pasta in this do-ahead salad that's perfect with grilled steak, chicken, or fish.

1. Combine the penne, green, red, and yellow bell peppers, and the scallions in a large bowl. Drizzle with the dressing and toss to coat. Refrigerate, covered, until chilled, at least 1 hour.

2. Line a serving platter with the lettuce; top with the pasta salad.

PER SERVING (ABOUT 1 CUP SALAD): 150 Cal, 1 g Fat, 0 g Sat Fat, 0 g Trans Fat, 0 mg Chol, 226 mg Sod, 34 g Carb, 4 g Fib, 5 g Prot, 28 mg Calc. *POINTS* value: *2.*

★

★ **tip** For a twist, toss the salad with an equal amount of our Roasted-Garlic Salad Dressing (page 176) instead of the ranch dressing.

MAKES 6 SERVINGS 🥬 🥕

- 3 cups cooked **whole-wheat penne**

- 1 **green bell pepper**, seeded and chopped

- 1 **red bell pepper**, seeded and chopped

- 1 **yellow bell pepper**, seeded and chopped

- 6 **scallions**, sliced

- ½ cup **fat-free ranch salad dressing**

- 6 **green leaf lettuce leaves**

Tex-Mex Sweet- and Red-Potato Salad

Warm roasted potatoes are tossed with a lemony-cilantro mayonnaise and a good pinch of south-of-the-border seasonings that are sure to tickle your taste buds. Serve with lean turkey burgers and sliced tomatoes.

1. Preheat the oven to 425°F. Spray a large jelly-roll pan with nonstick spray. Combine the red and sweet potatoes with 2 teaspoons of the oil in a large bowl; arrange in a single layer in the pan. Roast, tossing occasionally, until well browned and tender, 35–40 minutes. Transfer to a large bowl.

2. Meanwhile, heat the remaining 2 teaspoons oil in a large nonstick skillet over medium heat. Add the onions and cook, stirring occasionally, until golden and tender, 12–15 minutes. Transfer to the bowl with the potatoes.

3. Combine the mayonnaise, cilantro, lemon zest, salt, cumin, coriander, and cayenne in a small bowl. Add to the potato mixture and mix well. Serve warm or at room temperature.

PER SERVING (ABOUT ½ CUP): 142 Cal, 3 g Fat, 3 g Sat Fat, 0 g Trans Fat, 1 mg Chol, 247 mg Sod, 27 g Carb, 3 g Fib, 3 g Prot, 25 mg Calc. **POINTS** value: **2.**

★

★ **tip** Red Bliss potatoes are small red potatoes that are harvested before they reach maturity. Often called new potatoes, they are low in starch and sweet in flavor, making them ideal for roasting.

MAKES 8 SERVINGS

1 pound **Red Bliss potatoes**, cut into 1½-inch cubes

1 pound **sweet potatoes**, peeled and cut into 1½-inch cubes

4 teaspoons **olive oil**

2 **onions**, chopped

6 tablespoons **fat-free mayonnaise**

3 tablespoons chopped **fresh cilantro**

1 teaspoon grated **lemon zest**

½ teaspoon **salt**

½ teaspoon ground **cumin**

¼ teaspoon ground **coriander**

⅛ teaspoon **cayenne**

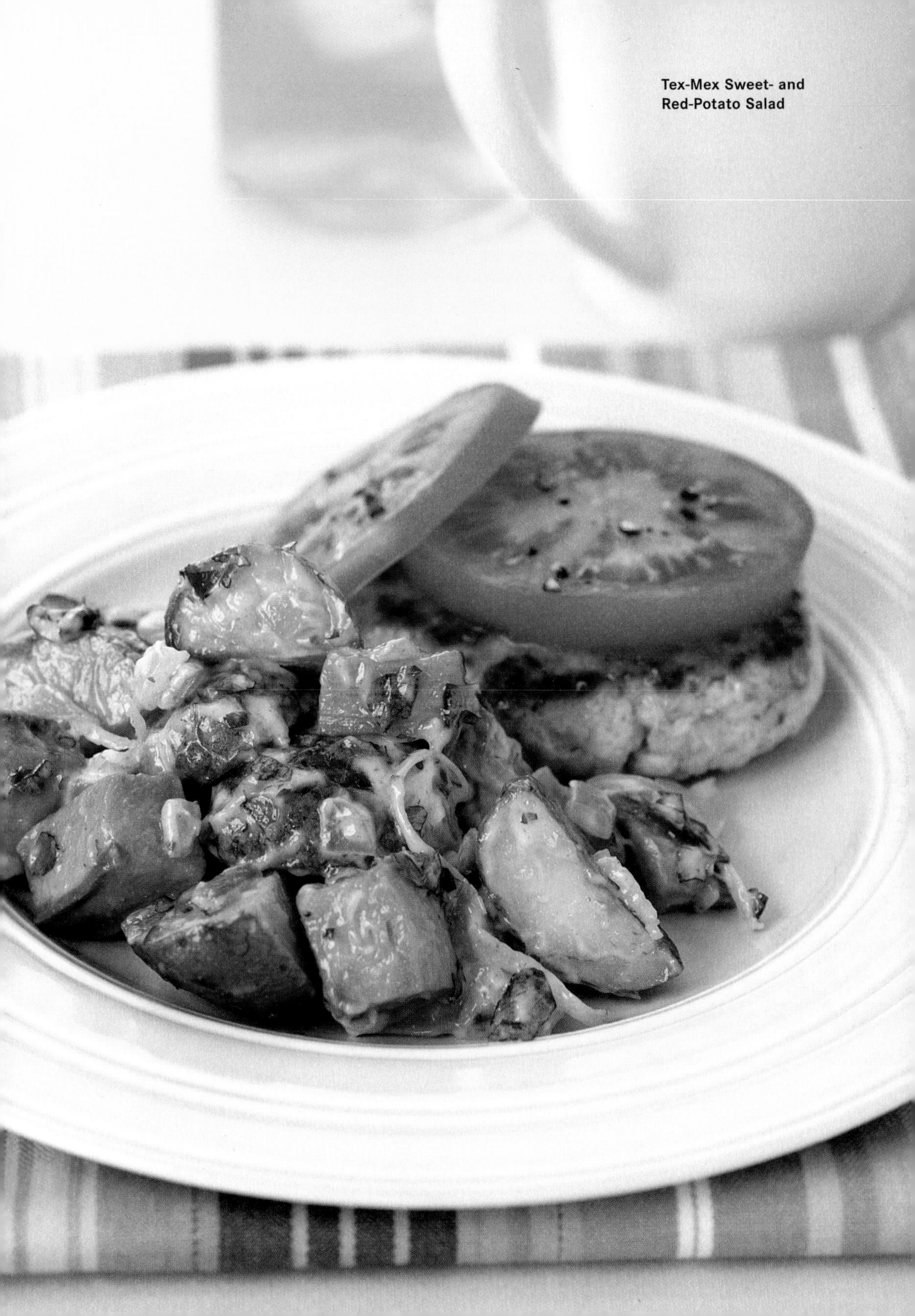

Tex-Mex Sweet- and
Red-Potato Salad

Roasted Asparagus with Greens and Citrus Dressing

Tender asparagus and crisp greens are tossed with a lively citrus dressing made with orange zest, lemon juice, and nutty-tasting flaxseed oil. It's the perfect spring salad to serve with loin lamb chops or a ham steak.

1. Preheat the oven to 400°F. Spray a large jelly-roll pan with canola oil nonstick spray. Arrange the asparagus in a single layer in the pan, spray with the nonstick spray, and sprinkle with ¼ teaspoon of the salt and ⅛ teaspoon of the pepper. Roast the asparagus, shaking the pan occasionally, until crisp-tender, 7–8 minutes.

2. Transfer the asparagus to a cutting board; let cool about 10 minutes. Cut the asparagus into 1½-inch pieces and transfer to a large bowl. Add the greens and scallions; toss to combine.

3. Grate the zest from the orange, then peel the orange and cut it into sections. Combine the zest, lemon juice, soy sauce, and the remaining ½ teaspoon salt and ⅛ teaspoon pepper in a small bowl. Gradually whisk in the oil until blended. Pour the dressing over the asparagus mixture. Stir in the orange sections and mix well.

PER SERVING (ABOUT 1 ⅓ CUPS): 79 Cal, 5 g Fat, 1 g Sat Fat, 0 g Trans Fat, 0 mg Chol, 565 mg Sod, 8 g Carb, 3 g Fib, 3 g Prot, 65 mg Calc. **POINTS** value: **1.**

MAKES 4 SERVINGS

1 pound fresh **asparagus**, trimmed

¾ teaspoon **salt**

¼ teaspoon freshly **ground pepper**

6 cups mesclun **salad greens**

2 **scallions**, chopped

1 navel **orange**

1 tablespoon **fresh lemon juice**

2 teaspoons reduced-sodium **soy sauce**

4 teaspoons **flaxseed oil**

Broccolini, Orange, and Arugula Salad

Broccolini (also called asparation) is a cross between broccoli and Chinese kale. It comes packaged in small bunches and has tender, slim stems that are completely edible. Broccolini has a mild, sweet taste and contains as much vitamin C as orange juice. It's also a good source of folate, vitamin A, and potassium.

1. Bring a large skillet half full of water to a boil. Add the broccolini, reduce the heat, and simmer until just crisp-tender, about 3 minutes. Drain and rinse under cold water.

2. Grate 1 teaspoon of zest from one of the oranges. Remove the peel and pith from all 3 oranges and slice each one into rounds.

3. Combine the zest, water, oil, vinegar, salt, and pepper in a large bowl; whisk to blend. Stir in the broccolini, sliced oranges, and onion; toss well.

4. Divide the arugula among 4 salad plates. Top each serving with one-quarter of the broccolini mixture. Drizzle any dressing from the bowl over the salads.

PER SERVING (1 CUP BROCCOLINI MIXTURE AND 1 ¼ CUPS ARUGULA): 108 Cal, 3 g Fat, 0 g Sat Fat, 0 g Trans Fat, 0 mg Chol, 173 mg Sod, 19 g Carb, 4 g Fib, 4 g Prot, 143 mg Calc.
POINTS value: **2**

★
★ **tip** You can substitute ½ pound broccoli, cut into florets, for the broccolini.

MAKES 4 SERVINGS

- 1 bunch **broccolini** (about ½ pound)
- 3 navel **oranges**
- 1 tablespoon **water**
- 2 teaspoons **extra-virgin olive oil**
- 2 teaspoons **rice-wine vinegar**
- ¼ teaspoon **salt**
- ¼ teaspoon freshly **ground pepper**
- ½ cup diced **Vidalia** or other **sweet onion**
- 1 (5-ounce) bag baby **arugula**

CHAPTER 4

Everyday Dinners

Spiced Pot Roast

Once you've assembled the spices, browned the beef, and cut the vegetables, this slow-simmering dish needs little attention. We've used frozen small white onions for convenience, but if you want to dress up the dish a bit, substitute an equal amount of peeled medium-sized shallots.

1. Spray a Dutch oven with olive oil nonstick spray and set over medium-high heat. Add the beef and cook, turning frequently, until browned, 8–10 minutes.

2. Stir in the broth, hot pepper sauce, coriander, salt, cinnamon, ginger, and ground pepper; bring to a boil. Reduce the heat to medium-low and simmer, covered, about 1½ hours.

3. Add the potatoes, carrots, onions, and garlic; mix well. Simmer, covered, until the beef and vegetables are fork-tender, 55–60 minutes. Transfer the beef to a cutting board; let stand 10 minutes. Cut into 6 slices and serve with the vegetables and broth.

PER SERVING (1 SLICE BEEF WITH 1 CUP VEGETABLES AND 2 TABLESPOONS BROTH): 258 Cal, 7 g Fat, 2 g Sat Fat, 1 g Trans Fat, 52 mg Chol, 530 mg Sod, 23 g Carb, 3 g Fib, 26 g Prot, 28 mg Calc. **POINTS** value: **5.**

MAKES 6 SERVINGS 🔥 🥩

- 1 (1½-pound) lean **eye-round roast**, trimmed of all visible fat

- 1 (14½-ounce) can reduced-sodium **beef broth**

- 1 teaspoon **hot pepper sauce**

- 1 teaspoon ground **coriander**

- ¾ teaspoon **salt**

- ¼ teaspoon **cinnamon**

- ¼ teaspoon ground **ginger**

- ¼ teaspoon freshly **ground pepper**

- 4 medium **red potatoes** (about 1 pound), each cut into 12 pieces

- 3 **carrots**, cut into 1-inch pieces

- 2 cups frozen small **white onions**

- 3 **garlic cloves**, minced

Beef Tenderloin with Mushrooms and Onions

Beef tenderloin is easy to prepare, provided you have an instant-read meat thermometer, an item readily available at the supermarket. The trick is to allow the roast to rest before carving: The beef will continue to cook as it stands, and the juices will have a chance to set.

1. Preheat the oven to 425°F. Spray the rack of a roasting pan with olive oil nonstick spray and place in the pan.

2. Sprinkle the beef with ½ teaspoon of the cumin, ½ teaspoon of the salt, and ⅛ teaspoon of the pepper. Heat 1 teaspoon of the oil in a large nonstick skillet over medium-high heat. Add the beef and cook, turning occasionally, until well browned, 6–8 minutes.

3. Place the beef on the rack in the pan and roast until an instant-read thermometer inserted in the center registers 135°F, 25–30 minutes. Transfer to a platter and let stand 10 minutes (The internal temperature will increase to 145°F for medium-rare.)

4. Meanwhile, heat the remaining 1 teaspoon oil in the same skillet over medium-high heat. Add the onions, mushrooms, garlic, and the remaining ¼ teaspoon cumin, ¼ teaspoon salt, and ⅛ teaspoon pepper; cook, stirring occasionally, until the onions and mushrooms are browned and softened, 9–10 minutes. Add the broth and Worcestershire sauce; bring to a boil. Boil until the liquid is reduced by about one-third, 7–8 minutes.

5. Cut the beef into 8 slices and serve with the sauce.

PER SERVING (2 SLICES BEEF WITH 3 TABLESPOONS SAUCE): 185 Cal, 9 g Fat, 3 g Sat Fat, 1 g Trans Fat, 42 mg Chol, 656 mg Sod, 9 g Carb, 2 g Fib, 18 g Prot, 27 mg Calc.
POINTS value: *4*.

MAKES 4 SERVINGS

- ¾ pound **beef tenderloin,** trimmed of all visible fat

- ¾ teaspoon ground **cumin**

- ¾ teaspoon **salt**

- ¼ teaspoon freshly **ground pepper**

- 2 teaspoons **olive oil**

- 2 **onions,** thinly sliced

- 1 (8-ounce) package sliced fresh **mushrooms**

- 3 **garlic cloves,** minced

- 1½ cups reduced-sodium **beef broth**

- 1 teaspoon **Worcestershire sauce**

Five-Spice London Broil

Our combination of chili powder, paprika, cumin, pepper, and cinnamon makes a delectable coating for steak, pork tenderloin, or chicken. Although you might think of cinnamon as a sweet spice, it's a traditional Mexican flavoring in many savory dishes. You don't really taste it, but it gives depth to the other spices.

1. Spray a broiler rack with canola oil nonstick spray; preheat the broiler.

2. Combine the chili powder, paprika, cumin, pepper, and cinnamon in a small bowl. Place the steak on a sheet of wax paper and sprinkle both sides with the spice mixture; let stand about 15 minutes.

3. Broil the steak 5 inches from the heat until an instant-read thermometer inserted in the center registers 145°F for medium-rare, 5–7 minutes on each side. Transfer the steak to a cutting board and let stand about 10 minutes. Slice thinly on an angle against the grain into 12–16 slices.

PER SERVING (3–4 SLICES OF STEAK): 202 Cal, 9 g Fat, 4 g Sat Fat, 1 g Trans Fat, 47 mg Chol, 68 mg Sod, 1 g Carb, 1 g Fib, 27 g Prot, 12 mg Calc. *POINTS* value: **5.**

★

★ **tip** If you prefer your steak more well done, broil it until an instant-read thermometer inserted in the center registers 160°F for medium, about 1 minute longer on each side.

MAKES 4 SERVINGS ☛

1 ½ teaspoons **chili powder**

½ teaspoon **paprika**

½ teaspoon ground **cumin**

¼ teaspoon freshly **ground pepper**

⅛ teaspoon **cinnamon**

1 (1-pound) lean **London broil** or **top round steak**, trimmed of all visible fat

4 POINTS VALUE

Beef and Vegetable Stew

If you're accustomed to using beef chuck in stews, consider lean top round steak as a healthier alternative. It's quite juicy, with good flavor and texture, so you'll achieve an equally satisfying result.

1. Preheat the oven to 325°F. Heat a medium nonstick Dutch oven over medium-high heat. Add the beef and cook, stirring constantly, until browned, about 5 minutes. Stir in the carrots, celery, onions, and parsnip; cook, stirring occasionally, about 5 minutes. Stir in the broth, tomatoes, rosemary, thyme, salt, and pepper.

2. Cover the pot and transfer to the oven. Bake until the beef and vegetables are fork-tender, about 1 ½ hours. Stir in the peas and bake until heated through, about 15 minutes longer.

PER SERVING (ABOUT 1 ½ CUPS): 240 Cal, 4 g Fat, 1 g Sat Fat, 1 g Trans Fat, 58 mg Chol, 623 mg Sod, 22 g Carb, 6 g Fib, 29 g Prot, 56 mg Calc. *POINTS* value: *4.*

★

★ **tip** Make a double or triple batch of this savory stew and freeze in containers for another meal or two.

MAKES 4 SERVINGS 🐄

- 1 pound lean **top round steak**, trimmed of all visible fat and cubed

- 2 **carrots**, cut into chunks

- 2 **celery** stalks, chopped

- 1 cup **frozen pearl onions**

- 1 **parsnip**, peeled and cut into chunks

- 1 ½ cups reduced-sodium **beef broth**

- 1 cup canned **crushed tomatoes**

- 1 teaspoon minced **fresh rosemary**

- 1 teaspoon minced **fresh thyme**

- ½ teaspoon **salt**

- ¼ teaspoon freshly **ground pepper**

- ½ (10-ounce) box **frozen peas**

Champion All-Beef Chili

Champion All-Beef Chili

This chili is hot; if you prefer it milder, omit or cut down on the jalapeños, or use less chili powder or a mild blend. You can serve this chili after it's simmered 45 minutes, but if you've got the time, let it go the distance. In fact, plan to make it a day or two ahead since it gets better as it mellows.

1. Heat a large nonstick saucepan or Dutch oven over medium-high heat. Add the beef and cook, stirring occasionally, until browned, about 5 minutes. Add the onions, garlic, and jalapeños; cook, stirring frequently, until the onions are softened, about 5 minutes. Add the chili powder, cumin, oregano, and cinnamon; stir until the spices coat the beef and vegetables.

2. Stir in the broth and bring to a boil. Reduce the heat and simmer, partially covered, until the beef is fork-tender, the broth is thickened, and the flavors are blended, 1–1½ hours. Sprinkle the chili with the scallions (if using).

PER SERVING (ABOUT 1 CUP): 191 Cal, 4 g Fat, 1 g Sat Fat, 1 g Trans Fat, 58 mg Chol, 391 mg Sod, 10 g Carb, 3 g Fib, 28 g Prot, 44 mg Calc. *POINTS* value: *4.*

★

★ **tip** If the chili's too hot and your mouth is on fire, eat some yogurt or drink some milk. Capsaicin, the substance in chiles that gives them their kick, bonds to the pain receptors in your mouth; the protein in milk and yogurt breaks that bond. Or top the hot chili with a grated mild cheese like fat-free mild cheddar, or add a dollop of fat-free sour cream or plain fat-free yogurt.

MAKES 4 SERVINGS

- 1 pound boneless lean **top round steak**, trimmed of all visible fat and cut into 1-inch chunks

- 2 **onions**, chopped

- 4 **garlic cloves**, minced

- 2–3 **jalapeño peppers**, seeded and minced (wear gloves to prevent irritation) or ¼ cup canned chopped green chiles

- 1–3 tablespoons **hot chili powder**

- 1 teaspoon ground **cumin**

- 1 teaspoon **dried oregano**

- ½ teaspoon **cinnamon**

- 3 cups reduced-sodium **beef broth**

- 2 **scallions**, sliced (optional)

Spaghetti Bolognese

Traditional Bolognese sauce takes hours to simmer, but our healthy version, chock-full of ground lean beef and vegetables, is ready in a fraction of the time. The sauce freezes beautifully, so make a double batch and thaw half in the microwave for an almost instant supper on a night when you get home late.

1. Spray a large nonstick skillet with canola oil nonstick spray and set over medium-high heat. Add the beef and cook, stirring frequently to break it up, until browned, 5–8 minutes. Add the onion and garlic; cook, stirring occasionally, until softened, about 5 minutes. Stir in the carrot and cook about 2 minutes. Stir in the mushrooms, tomatoes, tomato paste, basil, and oregano; bring to a boil. Reduce the heat and simmer, covered, 10 minutes. Add the milk and cook, uncovered, until the sauce is thickened, about 15 minutes longer. Stir in the salt and pepper.

2. Meanwhile, cook the spaghetti according to package directions. Drain, divide among 4 plates, and top with the sauce. Garnish with the basil leaves (if using).

PER SERVING (ABOUT 1 CUP PASTA AND ¾ CUP SAUCE): 402 Cal, 6 g Fat, 2 g Sat Fat, 0 g Trans Fat, 65 mg Chol, 510 mg Sod, 56 g Carb, 11 g Fib, 34 g Prot, 92 mg Calc. **_POINTS_ value: 8.**

★

★ **tip** Consider using fresh cremini mushrooms in the sauce. A dark-brown, slightly firmer variation of everyday white mushrooms, cremini mushrooms have a fuller flavor than their paler relatives.

MAKES 4 SERVINGS

¾ pound **ground lean beef** (5% or less fat)

1 **onion,** finely chopped

2 **garlic cloves,** minced

1 **carrot,** chopped

3 cups sliced fresh **mushrooms**

1 (14½-ounce) can diced **tomatoes**

1 tablespoon **tomato paste**

½ teaspoon **dried basil**

½ teaspoon **dried oregano**

¼ cup **fat-free milk**

½ teaspoon **salt**

¼ teaspoon freshly **ground pepper**

½ pound **whole-wheat spaghetti**

Fresh basil leaves for garnish (optional)

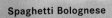

Dolmades

Dolmades, or stuffed grape leaves, are a favorite wrap throughout Greece and the Middle East. This savory filling features ground beef, bulgur, and tomatoes. Dolmades may be covered and refrigerated for up to 2 days before steaming.

1. Place a strainer over a 2-cup measure and drain the tomatoes, reserving the liquid. Chop the tomatoes and transfer to a large bowl.

2. Add enough water to the tomato liquid to make 2 cups, pour into a medium saucepan, and bring to a simmer. Add the bulgur and cumin; cook, covered, until the liquid is absorbed, 18–20 minutes. Add to the tomatoes.

3. Spray a large nonstick skillet with olive oil nonstick spray and set over medium-high heat. Add the onion and garlic; cook, stirring frequently, until softened, about 5 minutes. Add the beef and allspice; cook, stirring frequently to break up the beef, until it is no longer pink, about 6 minutes. Add the beef mixture, parsley, lemon juice, salt, and pepper to the bulgur mixture, and stir to combine.

4. Place the grape leaves in a pie plate, cover with the boiling water; then drain. Place a grape leaf, shiny-side down, on a cutting board, and trim off the stem. Spoon a scant ¼ cup of the bulgur mixture down the center lower third of the leaf. Rollup and tuck in the ends. Repeat with the remaining grape leaves and bulgur mixture to make a total of 24 dolmades. Place a steamer basket in a saucepan and arrange the rolled leaves, seam-side down, in the basket. Add ½ cup water to the saucepan and steam, covered, until the dolmades are heated through, about 20 minutes. Serve with the lemon wedges.

PER SERVING (4 DOLMADES): 157 Cal, 3 g Fat, 1 g Sat Fat, 0 g Trans Fat, 25 mg Chol, 718 mg Sod, 22 g Carb, 4 g Fib, 12 g Prot, 101 mg Calc. **POINTS** value: **3.**

MAKES 6 SERVINGS

1 (14½-ounce) can whole **tomatoes**

¾ cup **bulgur**

2 teaspoons **cumin seeds**, crushed

1 large **onion**, chopped

2 **garlic cloves**, minced

½ pound **ground lean beef** (5% or less fat)

¾ teaspoon ground **allspice**

¼ cup chopped **fresh parsley**

2 tablespoons **fresh lemon juice**

¾ teaspoon **salt**

¼ teaspoon freshly **ground pepper**

24 bottled **grape leaves**, rinsed and drained

1 cup boiling **water**

6 **lemon** wedges

Jerk Pork Tenderloin

Leftovers of this spicy Jamaican favorite are delicious reheated with a little tomato sauce and a dash of hot pepper sauce—if you can stand the heat! Try serving this with hot cooked brown rice and steamed fresh green beans.

1. Preheat the oven to 350°F. Combine the onion, cayenne, allspice, salt, thyme, cinnamon, nutmeg, and pepper in a small bowl.

2. Rub the spice mixture all over the tenderloin. Place in a shallow roasting pan and roast until an instant-read thermometer inserted in the center of the pork registers 160°F for medium, about 45 minutes. Transfer to a cutting board, cover loosely with foil, and let stand 10 minutes. Cut into 12–18 slices.

PER SERVING (2-3 SLICES OF PORK): 148 Cal, 4 g Fat, 1 g Sat Fat, 0 g Trans Fat, 65 mg Chol, 225 mg Sod, 3 g Carb, 1 g Fib, 24 g Prot, 19 mg Calc. *POINTS* value: *3*.

★

★ **tip** If you're pressed for time, use 6 lean boneless pork chops, trimmed of all visible fat. Or cut the tenderloin into 12 slices and, with the heel of your hand, press slices into ½-inch-thick medallions. Rub the spice mixture onto both sides of each medallion. Spray a large nonstick skillet with canola oil nonstick spray and set over medium-high heat. Sauté the medallions (in batches if necessary) until cooked through, 2 to 3 minutes on each side.

MAKES 6 SERVINGS 🔥 🍳

1 **onion**, minced

½ teaspoon **cayenne**

1 teaspoon ground **allspice**

½ teaspoon **salt**

½ teaspoon **dried thyme,** crumbled

½ teaspoon **cinnamon**

½ teaspoon grated **nutmeg**

½ teaspoon freshly **ground pepper**

1 (1½-pound) **pork tenderloin**, trimmed of all visible fat

Caribbean Pork with Sweet Potato

Sweet flavors go particularly well with pork; that's why we pair a tenderloin with sweet potatoes, Golden Delicious apple, and a Caribbean blend of sweet spices—ginger, allspice, and cinnamon. Serve this dish with a bowl of sautéed spinach or Swiss chard.

1. Preheat the oven to 400°F. Tear off 4 (12-inch) squares of parchment paper or foil. Fold each one in half lengthwise and cut into heart shapes with the fold running vertically down the center. Open each heart to lie flat.

2. Combine the sweet potato and apple in a medium bowl and spoon the mixture onto the center of one side of each heart.

3. Combine the broth, ginger, salt, allspice, and cinnamon in the same bowl. With the heel of your hand, press the pork slices until they are ¼ inch thick. Add to the spice mixture and toss to coat. Place the pork over the sweet-potato-and-apple mixture and sprinkle with the scallions. Fold the parchment over the pork. Starting at the top of each heart, make a series of tight, overlapping folds to seal the packets. Place on a baking sheet and bake until the pork is no longer pink and the sweet potatoes are tender, about 18 minutes. Open the packets carefully when testing for doneness, as steam will escape. Serve drizzled with any juices.

PER SERVING (3 SLICES PORK AND ¾ CUP SWEET-POTATO MIXTURE): 183 Cal, 4 g Fat, 1 g Sat Fat, 0 g Trans Fat, 56 mg Chol, 229 mg Sod, 17 g Carb, 3 g Fib, 19 g Prot, 24 mg Calc. **POINTS** value: **3.**

MAKES 4 SERVINGS

- 1 large **sweet potato**, peeled and thinly sliced

- 1 **Golden Delicious apple**, thinly sliced

- ¼ cup reduced-sodium **chicken broth**

- 1 teaspoon grated peeled **fresh ginger**

- ¼ teaspoon **salt**

- ¼ teaspoon ground **allspice**

- ⅛ teaspoon **cinnamon**

- ¾ pound **pork tenderloin**, trimmed of all visible fat and cut into 12 (½-inch-thick) slices

- 2 **scallions**, sliced

6 POINTS VALUE

New Orleans Red Beans and Rice

Red beans and rice is one of the best-known dishes to come out of Louisiana. The pairing of ham and beans creates a delicious gravy that flavors every kernel of rice. Legend has it that the musician Louis Armstrong signed correspondence "red beans and ricely yours" because he so loved this dish.

1. Cook the rice according to package directions, omitting any fat.

2. Meanwhile, heat the oil in a large nonstick skillet over medium-high heat. Add the onion, bell pepper, and garlic; cook, stirring occasionally, until softened, 3–4 minutes. Add the ham and cook, stirring occasionally, until it starts to brown, 4–5 minutes. Add the beans and Cajun seasoning; cook, stirring occasionally, until heated through, 1–2 minutes. Add the broth and cook until the liquid is almost completely absorbed, about 2 minutes. Serve over the rice.

PER SERVING (½ CUP BEAN MIXTURE WITH ½ CUP RICE): 297 Cal, 7 g Fat, 2 g Sat Fat, 0 g Trans Fat, 40 mg Chol, 861 mg Sod, 36 g Carb, 6 g Fib, 22 g Prot, 41 mg Calc. **POINTS** value: **6.**

★

★ **tip** Cajun seasoning—a blend of cayenne, paprika, garlic, and onion—can be found in the spice aisle of the supermarket. The amount of heat depends on the brand, so read the label carefully. You can also try this dish with Creole seasoning, which is a similar blend of spices.

MAKES 6 SERVINGS

1 cup **brown rice**

2 teaspoons **sunflower oil**

1 **onion**, chopped

1 **green bell pepper**, seeded and chopped

3 **garlic cloves**, minced

1 (1-pound) reduced-sodium boneless **ham steak**, trimmed of all visible fat and cut into ¼-inch pieces

1 (15½-ounce) can **red kidney beans**, rinsed and drained

1 teaspoon **Cajun seasoning**

½ cup reduced-sodium **chicken broth**

Pork Chops with Sautéed Apples and Sauerkraut

Pork Chops with Sautéed Apples and Sauerkraut

It's not uncommon for pork to be paired with apples and sauerkraut, but it's usually done in dishes that take hours to cook. That's not the case with these lean pork loin chops, which must be cooked quickly for the juiciest results.

1. Sprinkle the pork with ¼ teaspoon of the salt and ⅛ teaspoon of the pepper. Heat 1 teaspoon of the oil in a large nonstick skillet over medium-high heat. Add the pork and cook until browned and cooked through, 3–4 minutes on each side. Transfer to a plate and keep warm.

2. Heat the remaining 1 teaspoon oil in the skillet. Add the apples and cinnamon. Cook, stirring occasionally, until the apples begin to brown, 3–4 minutes. Add the sauerkraut, caraway seeds, and the remaining ¼ teaspoon salt and ⅛ teaspoon pepper. Cook until the sauerkraut begins to brown, 2–3 minutes. Serve with the pork.

PER SERVING (1 PORK CHOP WITH ½ CUP SAUERKRAUT-APPLE MIXTURE): 241 Cal, 9 g Fat, 3 g Sat Fat, 0 g Trans Fat, 67 mg Chol, 554 mg Sod, 16 g Carb, 3 g Fib, 24 g Prot, 37 mg Calc. *POINTS* value: **5.**

★

★ **tip** We find refrigerated sauerkraut to be vastly superior to the canned variety, which has a metallic aftertaste. Look for it in the dairy section of the supermarket.

MAKES 4 SERVINGS 🍴 🕐

4 (¼-pound) boneless center-cut **pork loin chops**, about ½-inch thick, trimmed of all visible fat

½ teaspoon **salt**

¼ teaspoon freshly **ground pepper**

2 teaspoons **safflower oil**

3 **Golden Delicious apples**, peeled, cored, and cut into ¼-inch-thick slices

¼ teaspoon **cinnamon**

1 cup **sauerkraut**, drained (See tip.)

½ teaspoon **caraway seeds**

Pasta Amatriciana

Amatriciana is a tomato sauce well-known for its smoky taste and zesty bite. Neither flavor is lacking in this healthy version, thanks to lean chopped Canadian bacon and a good pinch of crushed red pepper.

1. Heat the oil in a large nonstick saucepan over medium-high heat. Add the bacon and cook, stirring frequently, until heated through, about 1 minute. Stir in the onion and garlic; cook, covered, shaking the pan occasionally, until softened, about 5 minutes. Stir in the tomatoes, oregano, crushed red pepper, salt, ground pepper, and water; bring to a boil. Reduce the heat and simmer, uncovered, until the sauce is slightly reduced, about 5 minutes.

2. Meanwhile, cook the spaghetti according to package directions. Drain, toss with the sauce, and sprinkle with the parsley.

PER SERVING (ABOUT 1 ¼ CUPS): 261 Cal, 4 g Fat, 1 g Sat Fat, 0 g Trans Fat, 3 mg Chol, 518 mg Sod, 50 g Carb, 10 g Fib, 11 g Prot, 55 mg Calc. **POINTS** value: **5.**

MAKES 4 SERVINGS

2 teaspoons **olive oil**

1 slice **Canadian bacon**, trimmed of all visible fat and chopped

1 **onion**, chopped

1 **garlic clove**, minced

1 (14½-ounce) can diced **tomatoes**

½ teaspoon **dried oregano**

¼–½ teaspoon **crushed red pepper**

½ teaspoon **salt**

¼ teaspoon freshly **ground pepper**

¼ cup **water**

½ pound **whole-wheat spaghetti**

1 tablespoon chopped **fresh parsley**

Greek-Style Lamb with Yogurt Sauce

Savory lamb chops are served here with a refreshing cucumber-and-mint yogurt sauce. If fresh mint is unavailable, use an equal amount of fresh dill instead.

1. Remove the lamb chops from the refrigerator about ½ hour before cooking.

2. Meanwhile, puree the yogurt, cucumber, mint, scallions, garlic, ¼ teaspoon of the salt, and the crushed red pepper in a blender or food processor.

3. Spray the broiler rack with canola oil nonstick spray; preheat the broiler. Sprinkle the lamb with the remaining ¼ teaspoon salt and the ground pepper. Broil the lamb 3–4 inches from heat until done to taste, 4–5 minutes on each side for medium-rare and 5–7 minutes on each side for well done. Serve, topped with the sauce and sprinkled lightly with the paprika.

PER SERVING (1 CHOP AND ⅓ CUP SAUCE): 232 Cal, 11 g Fat, 4 g Sat Fat, 0 g Trans Fat, 78 mg Chol, 399 mg Sod, 5 g Carb, 1 g Fib, 26 g Prot, 113 mg Calc. *POINTS* value: **5.**

★

★ **tip** If you opt to grill the lamb, do so over a hot fire and the cooking time will remain the same.

MAKES 4 SERVINGS

4 (5-ounce) bone-in **loin lamb chops**, trimmed of all visible fat, about 1-inch thick

¾ cup plain **fat-free yogurt**

½ **cucumber**, peeled, seeded, and chopped

¼ cup **fresh mint**

3 **scallions**, sliced

1 **garlic clove**, chopped

½ teaspoon **salt**

¼ teaspoon **crushed red pepper**

Freshly **ground pepper** to taste

½ teaspoon **paprika**

Turkish Lamb Kebabs

Lean chunks of lamb are marinated in lemon juice, garlic, and herbs, then threaded on skewers with onion and bell pepper. The recipe can easily be doubled if you're expecting company. If you're not a lamb lover, try it with boneless sirloin steak trimmed of all visible fat. Chunks of zucchini and cherry tomatoes can be substituted for the onion and bell pepper.

1. To prepare the marinade, puree the onion, lemon juice, garlic, dill, oregano, paprika, and pepper in a blender or food processor. Transfer to a zip-close plastic bag and add the lamb. Squeeze out the air and seal the bag; turn to coat the lamb. Refrigerate, turning the bag occasionally, at least 3 hours or up to overnight.

2. Soak 4 (10-inch) bamboo skewers in water about 30 minutes so they won't burn under the broiler.

3. Spray the broiler rack with canola oil nonstick spray; preheat the broiler. Alternately thread the lamb, onion, and bell pepper on the skewers. Broil the skewers 3–4 inches from heat until the lamb is done to taste, 3–4 minutes on each side for medium-rare and 4–5 minutes on each side for well done.

PER SERVING (1 SKEWER): 183 Cal, 8 g Fat, 3 g Sat Fat, 0 g Trans Fat, 73 mg Chol, 59 mg Sod, 5 g Carb, 2 g Fib, 24 g Prot, 20 mg Calc. *POINTS* value: **4.**

★

★ **tip** Serve the kebabs with yogurt sprinkled with fresh dill sprigs and whole-wheat couscous, as pictured (⅓ cup plain fat-free yogurt for each serving will increase the *POINTS* value by 1 and ⅔ cup cooked couscous will increase the *POINTS* value by 2).

MAKES 4 SERVINGS 🔥

- 1 **onion**, chopped
- 2 tablespoons **fresh lemon juice**
- 5–6 **garlic cloves**, minced
- 1 tablespoon finely chopped **fresh dill**
- 1 tablespoon **dried oregano**
- 1 tablespoon **paprika**
- ½ teaspoon freshly **ground pepper**
- 1 pound boneless **leg of lamb**, trimmed of all visible fat and cut into 1½-inch cubes
- 1 **onion**, cut into 8 wedges
- 1 **red bell pepper**, seeded and cut into 1-inch pieces

Turkish Lamb Kebabs

Veal Paprikash

This Hungarian classic is traditionally prepared with chicken, but its elegance also makes it particularly suitable for veal. The key to a great paprikash is sweet paprika, preferably from Hungary, which is considered by many to be superior to other commercial brands. You can find sweet Hungarian paprika in gourmet stores and some supermarkets.

1. Heat 1 teaspoon of the oil in a large Dutch oven over medium-high heat. Add the veal and cook, turning occasionally, until browned, about 4 minutes. Transfer to a plate.

2. Heat the remaining 1 teaspoon oil in the Dutch oven. Add the carrots, celery, onion, and garlic; cook, stirring occasionally, until softened, 5–6 minutes. Add the veal, broth, paprika, salt, and pepper; bring to a boil. Reduce the heat to medium-low and simmer, partially covered, until the veal and vegetables are fork-tender, about 1 hour 20 minutes. Remove the Dutch oven from the heat and stir in the sour cream and mustard.

PER SERVING (1 CUP): 231 Cal, 6 g Fat, 2 g Sat Fat, 0 g Trans Fat, 84 mg Chol, 985 mg Sod, 15 g Carb, 3 g Fib, 28 g Prot, 104 mg Calc. *POINTS* value: **5.**

MAKES 4 SERVINGS

- 2 teaspoons **olive oil**
- 1 pound boneless **veal round steak**, trimmed of all visible fat and cut into ¾-inch cubes
- 2 **carrots**, chopped
- 2 **celery** stalks, chopped
- 1 **onion**, chopped
- 2 **garlic cloves**, minced
- 1 (14½-ounce) can reduced-sodium **beef broth**
- 1 tablespoon **paprika**
- 1 teaspoon **salt**
- ¼ teaspoon freshly **ground pepper**
- ¾ cup **fat-free sour cream**
- 2 teaspoons **Dijon mustard**

Perfect Roast Chicken

Who can resist roast chicken, especially when it's prepared with lemon, garlic, and fresh thyme? Our secret is roasting the bird on a rack, which allows a tremendous amount of fat to drain off the skin yet keeps the bird moist and succulent.

1. Preheat the oven to 375°F.

2. Rinse the chicken inside and out; pat dry with paper towels. Sprinkle the outside with the salt and pepper. Place the rack of a roasting pan in the pan and place the chicken, breast-side up, on the rack. Prick 1 lemon in several places with a fork and place it the cavity of the chicken along with the garlic. Carefully lift the skin from the chicken and tuck the thyme sprigs under the skin. Squeeze the juice from the remaining lemon over the chicken.

3. Roast the chicken, basting occasionally with the pan juices, until an instant-read thermometer inserted in a thigh registers 180°F, 1–1½ hours. (Cover loosely with foil if the chicken browns too quickly.) Transfer the chicken to a cutting board. Let stand 15 minutes before carving. Remove the skin before eating.

PER SERVING (⅙ OF CHICKEN): 194 Cal, 8 g Fat, 2 g Sat Fat, 0 g Trans Fat, 90 mg Chol, 281 mg Sod, 0 g Carb, 0 g Fib, 29 g Prot, 16 mg Calc. *POINTS* value: *5.*

MAKES 6 SERVINGS 🍳

1 (3½-pound) **chicken**

½ teaspoon **salt**

¼ teaspoon freshly **ground pepper**

2 **lemons**

4 **garlic cloves**, peeled

2 sprigs **fresh thyme**, or ½ teaspoon dried, crumbled

Roast Chicken with Garlic and Potatoes

In this recipe, five cloves of sweet roasted garlic accompany each serving, to be spread on the chicken. The entrée is complete with vegetables, so you need serve only a green salad alongside.

1. Preheat the oven to 425°F. Spray a large roasting pan with olive oil nonstick spray. Combine the chicken, potatoes, garlic, carrots, rosemary, salt, and pepper in the pan. Add the oil and toss to coat.

2. Bake, stirring occasionally, until the vegetables are tender and the chicken is cooked through, about 50 minutes.

PER SERVING (2 PIECES CHICKEN AND ABOUT ¾ CUP VEGETABLES): 402 Cal, 14 g Fat, 3 g Sat Fat, 0 g Trans Fat, 116 mg Chol, 720 mg Sod, 24 g Carb, 4 g Fib, 42 g Prot, 66 mg Calc. *POINTS* value: *8.*

★

★ **tip** A medium-bodied red wine, such as Merlot, would go beautifully with this dish. Enjoy 1 small glass (or ½ cup) and up the *POINTS* value by 2.

MAKES 4 SERVINGS ☛

- 1 (3-pound) **chicken**, skinned, cut into 8 pieces, and trimmed of all visible fat

- 1 pound small **red potatoes**, scrubbed and quartered

- 20 **garlic cloves**, unpeeled

- 2 **carrots**, sliced

- 2 sprigs **fresh rosemary**

- 1 teaspoon **salt**

- ¼ teaspoon freshly **ground pepper**

- 4 teaspoons **olive oil**

3 POINTS VALUE

Chicken and Vegetables en Papillote

The French cooking technique *en papillote* refers to food baked in a wrapping. We use this low-fat, high-moisture method to wrap skinless, boneless chicken breasts, shallots, red bell pepper, and snow peas in heavy-duty foil (or parchment paper). For extra flavor, add a sprig of fresh thyme to each package.

1. Preheat the oven to 450°F. Spray a large nonstick skillet with canola oil nonstick spray and set over medium-high heat. Add the snow peas, bell pepper, shallots, and broth; cook, stirring constantly, until the vegetables just begin to soften, 2–3 minutes.

2. Place 4 (12-inch) squares of heavy-duty foil or parchment paper on a work surface. Place a chicken breast in the center of each square and sprinkle with the salt and pepper. Top with the snow-pea mixture, drizzling any pan juices over the vegetables, and sprinkle with the parsley. Make a packet by bringing the sides of the foil up to meet in the center and folding over the edges, then folding the edges of the ends together. Allowing room for the packets to expand, crimp the edges.

3. Bake the packets until the chicken is cooked through, about 18 minutes. Open the packets carefully when testing for doneness, as steam will escape. Serve, drizzled with any juices.

PER SERVING (1 PACKET): 145 Cal, 3 g Fat, 1 g Sat Fat, 0 g Trans Fat, 63 mg Chol, 387 mg Sod, 5 g Carb, 1 g Fib, 24 g Prot, 26 mg Calc. *POINTS* value: **3.**

★
★ **tip** If you don't have heavy-duty foil or parchment paper on hand, use a double thickness of regular foil.

MAKES 4 SERVINGS

1 cup fresh **snow peas**, trimmed

1 **red bell pepper**, seeded and diced

2 **shallots**, minced

¼ cup reduced-sodium **chicken broth**

4 (¼-pound) skinless boneless **chicken breasts**, trimmed of all visible fat

½ teaspoon **salt**

¼ teaspoon freshly **ground pepper**

1 tablespoon chopped **fresh parsley**

Shiitake-Chicken Stir-Fry

3 POINTS VALUE

Shiitake-Chicken Stir-Fry

Kids will love this easy stir-fry—of tender strips of chicken, broccoli, red bell pepper, and shiitake mushrooms—because it's not at all spicy. Fresh shiitake mushrooms have large dark-brown caps and tough, almost inedible stems. Always separate the two before cooking, but don't discard the stems. Toss them into soups and sauces, where they'll release their magnificent, smoky flavor, but remove them before serving (as you would a bay leaf).

1. Heat a large nonstick skillet or wok over medium-high heat until a drop of water sizzles. Pour in the oil and swirl to coat the pan. Add the garlic and ginger and stir-fry until just fragrant, about 15 seconds. Add the bell pepper, broccoli, mushrooms, and scallions; stir-fry until the vegetables are crisp-tender, about 3 minutes. Transfer the vegetables to a plate, cover and keep warm.

2. Add the chicken to the wok and stir-fry, adding the broth as needed to prevent sticking, until lightly browned and cooked through, about 4 minutes. Add the vegetables, soy sauce, salt, and pepper; cook until the vegetables are heated through and the soy sauce coats everything, about 2 minutes.

PER SERVING (ABOUT 1¼ CUPS): 156 Cal, 5 g Fat, 1 g Sat Fat, 0 g Trans Fat, 47 mg Chol, 502 mg Sod, 10 g Carb, 2 g Fib, 19 g Prot, 35 mg Calc. *POINTS* value: *3.*

★
★ **tip** Serve the stir-fry with brown rice, as pictured (½ cup per serving will up the *POINTS* value by 2).

MAKES 4 SERVINGS

2 teaspoons **canola oil**

3 **garlic cloves**, minced

1 (½-inch) piece **fresh ginger**, peeled and grated

1 **red bell pepper**, seeded and thinly sliced

1 cup **broccoli** florets

1 cup sliced fresh **shiitake mushrooms**

8 **scallions**, thinly sliced

¾ pound skinless boneless **chicken breasts**, trimmed of all visible fat and cut into strips

1–2 tablespoons reduced-sodium **chicken broth** or water

1 tablespoon reduced-sodium **soy sauce**

½ teaspoon **salt**

¼ teaspoon freshly **ground pepper**

Italian Skillet Chicken

Chicken strips simmer in a simple tomato sauce with lots of veggies and fresh basil. We use skinless, boneless chicken breasts, but you could use chicken tenders.

Heat the oil in a large nonstick skillet over medium-high heat. Add the onions, carrot, and celery; cook, stirring occasionally, until softened, about 10 minutes. Add the chicken and cook, stirring occasionally, until opaque, about 5 minutes. Stir in the tomatoes, basil, salt, and pepper. Reduce the heat and simmer, stirring occasionally, until the flavors are blended and the chicken is cooked through, about 10 minutes.

PER SERVING (ABOUT 1 ½ CUPS): 186 Cal, 5 g Fat, 1 g Sat Fat, 0 g Trans Fat, 47 mg Chol, 492 mg Sod, 17 g Carb, 4 g Fib, 20 g Prot, 71 mg Calc. **POINTS** value: **3.**

★

★ **tip** Whole-wheat penne makes a nice accompaniment to this dish (⅔ cup cooked penne for each serving will increase the **POINTS** value by 2).

MAKES 4 SERVINGS 👉

2 teaspoons **olive oil**

2 **onions**, chopped

1 **carrot**, chopped

1 **celery** stalk, sliced

¾ pound skinless boneless **chicken breasts**, trimmed of all visible fat and cut into strips

1 (14½-ounce) can **crushed tomatoes**

1 tablespoon chopped **fresh basil** or 1 teaspoon dried

½ teaspoon **salt**

¼ teaspoon freshly **ground pepper**

3 POINTS VALUE

Roast Turkey Breast with Garlic and Herbs

Whole turkey breasts are an increasingly popular, easy, and inexpensive way to feed a large gathering. Here, fragrant herbs and garlic smother the turkey breast and perfume the kitchen with a mouthwatering scent as the turkey roasts.

1. Preheat the oven to 400°F. Spray the rack of a roasting pan with olive oil nonstick spray and place it in the pan.

2. Combine the garlic, sage, oregano, oil, lemon zest, salt, and pepper in a small bowl; stir until the consistency of a paste. Carefully lift the skin from the turkey and rub the garlic-herb paste evenly under the skin. Place the turkey, skin-side up, on the rack in the pan.

3. Roast the turkey 10 minutes. Reduce the oven temperature to 325°F and roast until an instant-read thermometer inserted in the center of the breast registers 170°F, about 1 hour 40 minutes.

4. Transfer the turkey to a large cutting board; let stand 10 minutes before carving. Remove the skin before eating.

PER SERVING (ABOUT 2 SLICES): 157 Cal, 2 g Fat, 0 g Sat Fat, 0 g Trans Fat, 88 mg Chol, 249 mg Sod, 1 g Carb, 0 g Fib, 32 g Prot, 21 mg Calc. *POINTS* value: *3.*

★

★ **tip** This turkey breast makes a terrific sandwich the next day. Spread 2 slices of high-fiber, whole-grain bread with Dijon mustard, and top one slice with 2 slices of turkey, sliced tomato, and arugula leaves. Cover with the remaining slice of bread.

MAKES 12 SERVINGS 🍴

4 **garlic cloves**, minced

2 tablespoons chopped **fresh sage**

2 tablespoons chopped **fresh oregano**

1 tablespoon **extra-virgin olive oil**

2 teaspoons grated **lemon zest**

1 teaspoon **salt**

½ teaspoon freshly **ground pepper**

1 (4½- to 5-pound) bone-in **turkey breast**

3 POINTS VALUE

Fiesta Stuffed Cabbage

The whole family will love these Tex-Mex-style cabbage rolls stuffed with ground turkey and barley. Be sure to use Savoy cabbage in this recipe, as its leaves are especially pliable.

1. Place the cabbage in a large pot and cover with enough water to fill the pot half full. Bring to a boil; reduce the heat and cook until the outer leaves are pliable, about 5 minutes. Loosen and remove 12 leaves with tongs; transfer to a large bowl. Reserve the remaining cabbage for another use.

2. Meanwhile, cook the barley according to package directions.

3. Heat the oil in a large skillet over medium-high heat. Add the turkey, onion, and garlic; cook, stirring frequently to break up the turkey, until it is no longer pink and the onion is tender, about 10 minutes. Stir in the barley and taco seasoning.

4. Preheat the oven to 375°F. Spoon about ⅓ cup of the barley mixture onto the center of each cabbage leaf, fold in the sides, and roll up burrito style. Place, seam-side down, in a 9 x 13-inch baking dish. Repeat with the remaining barley mixture and cabbage leaves, placing the rolls close to one another in the baking dish. Cover with the salsa and bake until the cabbage is very tender, about 25 minutes.

PER SERVING (2 ROLLS): 166 Cal, 2 g Fat, 0 g Sat Fat, 0 g Trans Fat, 37 mg Chol, 655 mg Sod, 22 g Carb, 3 g Fib, 16 g Prot, 43 mg Calc. *POINTS* value: *3.*

MAKES 6 SERVINGS

- 1 head **Savoy cabbage**, cored

- ½ cup **quick-cooking barley**

- 2 teaspoons **olive oil**

- ¾ pound ground lean skinless **turkey breast**

- 1 small **onion**, chopped

- 1 **garlic clove**, minced

- 1 (1¼-ounce) package reduced-sodium **taco seasoning mix**

- 1 cup **fat-free salsa**

Fiesta Stuffed Cabbage

Turkey Cutlets with Roasted Pepper and Mozzarella

Here's a different take on turkey: Ultra-thin cutlets are sprinkled with parsley, lemon zest, and garlic, then rolled up with roasted red pepper and mozzarella. Whole roasted peppers from a jar are best here. To make rolling easy, cut each slice so it's slightly smaller than the cutlet.

1. Preheat the oven to 400°F. Spray a baking dish with olive oil nonstick spray. Combine the parsley, garlic, rosemary, and lemon zest in a small bowl.

2. Place the turkey cutlets between 2 sheets of wax paper and pound gently to flatten slightly. Remove the wax paper. Rub each cutlet with the parsley mixture, place a red- pepper slice on each cutlet, and sprinkle with the cheese. Roll up gently from the wide end and secure the rolls with toothpicks. Place, seam-side down, in the baking dish. Bake until cooked through, about 20 minutes.

PER SERVING (1 TURKEY ROLL): 152 Cal, 1 g Fat, 0 g Sat Fat, 0 g Trans Fat, 77 mg Chol, 176 mg Sod, 3 g Carb, 0 g Fib, 32 g Prot, 144 mg Calc. *POINTS* value: *3.*

MAKES 4 SERVINGS

- ¼ cup packed chopped flat-leaf **parsley**

- 1 **garlic clove**, minced

- ¼ teaspoon **dried rosemary**, crumbled

- 1 strip **lemon zest**, coarsely chopped

- 4 (¼-pound) **turkey cutlets**, trimmed of all visible fat

- 4 slices **roasted red pepper**

- ½ cup shredded **fat-free mozzarella cheese**

Tex-Mex Salmon with Sweet Peppers

Salmon steaks are always a good value, and they are often on sale at the supermarket. Salmon is so easy to cook, too, as is evident in this recipe, where we briefly marinate, then bake the fish on a bed of roasted peppers.

1. Puree the cilantro, lime juice, cumin, salt, hot pepper sauce, and water in a blender or food processor. Transfer to a zip-close plastic bag and add the salmon. Squeeze out the air and seal the bag; turn to coat the salmon. Refrigerate, turning the bag occasionally, 1 hour.

2. Preheat the oven to 400°F. Spray a 9 x 13-inch baking dish with olive oil nonstick spray. Arrange the bell peppers in a single layer in the dish. Bake, turning once, 20 minutes.

3. Drain the salmon and discard the marinade. Place the salmon on top of the bell peppers. Bake until the fish is just opaque in the center, 10–12 minutes. Remove the skin before eating.

PER SERVING (½ SALMON STEAK AND ABOUT 1 CUP PEPPERS): 183 Cal, 5 g Fat, 1 g Sat Fat, 0 g Trans Fat, 65 mg Chol, 386 mg Sod, 9 g Carb, 2 g Fib, 26 g Prot, 42 mg Calc. **POINTS** value: **4.**

★

★ **tip** Here's a trick for coring and seeding bell peppers: Hold the pepper upright, by the stem if it has one and with a sharp knife, cut off the 4 sides. You'll be left with the core, nearly all the seeds and membranes, and the bottom in one neat little package you can throw away.

MAKES 4 SERVINGS

- 3 cups **fresh cilantro** leaves
- 2 tablespoons **fresh lime juice**
- 1 teaspoon ground **cumin**
- ½ teaspoon **salt**
- ⅛ teaspoon **hot pepper sauce**
- ¼ cup **water**
- 2 (½–¾-pound) **salmon steaks**
- 2 **yellow bell peppers,** seeded and sliced
- 2 **red bell peppers,** seeded and sliced

Lemony Salmon with Yogurt-Dill Sauce

You'll need a whole lemon to make this quick-fix dish. If you're short of fresh dill, don't substitute the dried stuff; use an equal amount of fresh tarragon or flat-leaf parsley instead.

1. Grate ¼ teaspoon zest from the lemon. Cut the lemon in half, juice one of the halves to get 2 teaspoons of fresh juice, and set the remaining half aside.

2. Combine the lemon zest, lemon juice, yogurt, dill, and ¼ teaspoon of the salt in a small bowl.

3. Squeeze the reserved lemon half over the salmon and sprinkle with the remaining ¼ teaspoon salt and the pepper. Spray a large nonstick skillet with canola oil nonstick spray and set over medium-high heat. Add the salmon and cook until just opaque in the center, about 4 minutes on each side. For salmon steaks, remove the skin before eating. Serve with the sauce.

PER SERVING (1 SALMON STEAK WITH 2 TABLESPOONS SAUCE): 147 Cal, 4 g Fat, 1 g Sat Fat, 0 g Trans Fat, 58 mg Chol, 362 mg Sod, 3 g Carb, 0 g Fib, 24 g Prot, 60 mg Calc.
POINTS value: **3.**

MAKES 4 SERVINGS 🍴 🕐

1 **lemon**

½ cup plain **fat-free yogurt**

1 tablespoon chopped **fresh dill**

½ teaspoon **salt**

4 (4–6-ounce) **salmon steaks** or 1 pound skinless salmon fillet

¼ teaspoon freshly **ground pepper**

Salmon Niçoise Salad

Canned salmon, a terrific source of calcium, replaces the canned tuna in this world-famous salad from the French Riviera. Cook the eggs and steam the green beans up to a day ahead of time, and you've got a meal that's ready in less than 20 minutes.

1. Place the salmon in a small bowl. Discard any skin; then mash the fish and its bones with a fork.

2. Arrange the mesclun, tomatoes, and green beans on 4 plates. Arrange the salmon and 2 egg quarters on each plate, scatter each serving with the olives and capers, and sprinkle with the parsley.

3. Combine the vinegar, oil, mustard, salt, and pepper in a small bowl; drizzle over the salads.

PER SERVING (1 SALAD): 195 Cal, 13 g Fat, 3 g Sat Fat, 0 g Trans Fat, 117 mg Chol, 605 mg Sod, 10 g Carb, 3 g Fib, 13 g Prot, 180 mg Calc. **POINTS** value: **4.**

★ **tip** Be sure to store and serve tomatoes at room temperature—refrigerating them destroys their flavor.

MAKES 4 SERVINGS

1 (6-ounce) can **red salmon**

4 cups mesclun **salad greens**

4 **plum tomatoes,** quartered

1 cup (2-inch lengths) trimmed fresh **green beans,** steamed

2 large **eggs,** hard-cooked and quartered

12 **niçoise olives**

2 teaspoons drained rinsed **capers**

1 tablespoon chopped **fresh parsley**

2 tablespoons **red-wine vinegar**

1 tablespoon **olive oil**

1 teaspoon **Dijon mustard**

½ teaspoon **salt**

¼ teaspoon freshly **ground pepper**

Potato-Crusted Salmon

5
POINTS
VALUE

Potato-Crusted Salmon

Wafer-thin slices of potato are wrapped around salmon fillets. Then each "bundle" is broiled until the potatoes are crisp and golden and the salmon is cooked through. Serve with steamed asparagus and sautéed cherry tomatoes.

1. Place the potatoes in a colander and toss with the lemon juice and salt. Let stand until the potatoes are soft and pliable, about 10 minutes. Pat the potatoes dry with paper towels.

2. Spray a large baking sheet with olive oil nonstick spray. Tear off 4 (12-inch) squares of wax paper and spray with the nonstick spray. Arrange all but 4 of the potato slices horizontally, shingle-fashion, to form a 5 x 9-inch rectangle on each square; spray the potatoes with the nonstick spray. Place 1 piece of salmon vertically across each rectangle of potatoes, and spread with the mustard. Lift the right side of each square of wax paper and fold it over the salmon, covering it with the potatoes. Lightly press the wax paper to help the potatoes adhere to the fish and peel back the wax paper. Repeat with the left side of the wax paper. Lay the remaining 4 potato slices over each seam where the shingled potatoes meet, and brush with the oil. With a spatula, carefully transfer each bundle to the baking sheet, turning the bundles over so that the side with the additional potato slice lies on the baking sheet. Cover loosely with plastic wrap and refrigerate so the potatoes set, about 30 minutes.

3. Spray the broiler pan with olive oil nonstick spray and preheat the broiler. Spray the potatoes with the nonstick spray. Broil 6 inches from the heat until the potatoes are golden and crisp and the salmon is opaque in the center, about 5 minutes on each side.

PER SERVING (1 PIECE SALMON): 263 Cal, 7 g Fat, 1 g Sat Fat, 0 g Trans Fat, 65 mg Chol, 364 mg Sod, 23 g Carb, 3 g Fib, 27 g Prot, 49 mg Calc. *POINTS* value: *5.*

MAKES 4 SERVINGS

2 large **baking potatoes,** peeled and thinly sliced lengthwise

2 teaspoons **fresh lemon juice**

¼ teaspoon **salt**

1 pound skinless **salmon fillet,** cut into 4 pieces

4 teaspoons **Dijon mustard**

2 teaspoons **olive oil**

Marinated Tuna with Roasted-Corn and Red-Pepper Relish

Not all fish are as suitable for marinating as tuna. Its firm, meat-like texture makes it an ideal candidate for piquant marinades, like this simple one made with balsamic vinegar, Dijon mustard, and fiery crushed red pepper. This marinade also complements the natural sweetness of the roasted-vegetable relish.

1. To prepare the marinade, combine the vinegar, water, mustard, crushed red pepper, salt, and ground pepper in a large zip-close plastic bag. Transfer 2 tablespoons of the marinade to a medium bowl and reserve. Add the tuna to the bag, squeeze out the air and seal the bag; turn to coat the tuna. Refrigerate, turning the bag occasionally, 1 hour.

2. Spray a nonstick baking sheet and the broiler rack with canola oil nonstick spray; preheat the broiler. Arrange the corn in a thin layer on the baking sheet. Broil 6 inches from the heat, stirring often, until the corn begins to brown, about 3 minutes. Add the corn and roasted pepper to the reserved marinade; set aside.

3. Drain the tuna and discard the marinade. Place the tuna on the broiler rack. Broil 6 inches from the heat, turning once, until done to taste, 3–4 minutes on each side for medium-rare.

4. Divide the endive among 4 plates; top with the tuna and relish.

PER SERVING (1 PIECE TUNA, GENEROUS ½ CUP RELISH, AND ½ CUP ENDIVE): 272 Cal, 3 g Fat, 1 g Sat Fat, 0 g Trans Fat, 66 mg Chol, 380 mg Sod, 27 g Carb, 3 g Fib, 37 g Prot, 49 mg Calc. *POINTS* value: *5.*

MAKES 4 SERVINGS

¼ cup **balsamic vinegar**

2 tablespoons **water**

1½ teaspoons **Dijon mustard**

½–1 teaspoon **crushed red pepper**

¼ teaspoon **salt**

¼ teaspoon freshly **ground pepper**

4 (5-ounce, ½-inch thick) **tuna steaks**

2 cups fresh or thawed frozen **corn kernels**

1 cup chopped **roasted red pepper**

2 cups torn **curly endive** or **chicory**

Marinated Tuna with Roasted-Corn
and Red-Pepper Relish

Tuna-Noodle Bake

Call this pure comfort food with a bonus dose of veggies. We use frozen mixed vegetables, so there's little knife work to bother with.

1. Preheat the oven to 375°F. Spray a shallow 2-quart casserole dish with canola oil nonstick spray. Cook the noodles according to package directions, adding the mixed vegetables during the last minute of cooking. Drain and pour into the casserole dish. Scatter the tuna over the top.

2. Lightly beat the milk and eggs in a medium bowl. Stir in about ½ cup of the cheese, the salt, and pepper; pour over the pasta mixture. Sprinkle with the remaining ¼ cup cheese. Bake, uncovered, until a knife inserted in the center comes out clean and the top is golden brown, about 50 minutes. Let stand about 5 minutes, then cut into four servings.

PER SERVING (¼ OF CASSEROLE): 313 Cal, 5 g Fat, 1 g Sat Fat, 0 g Trans Fat, 142 mg Chol, 769 mg Sod, 38 g Carb, 7 g Fib, 30 g Prot, 357 mg Calc. *POINTS* value: *6*.

★
★ **tip** Whole-wheat egg noodles are available in health food stores and some supermarkets.

MAKES 4 SERVINGS

- 2 cups wide **whole-wheat egg noodles**

- 1 (16-ounce) bag frozen **mixed vegetables**

- 1 (6-ounce) can water-packed solid white **tuna**, drained and flaked

- 1½ cups **fat-free milk**

- 2 large **eggs**

- ¾ cup shredded **fat-free sharp cheddar cheese**

- ½ teaspoon **salt**

- ¼ teaspoon freshly **ground pepper**

Southern-Style Fish and Chips

This down-home supper of "oven-fried" catfish and crispy potato fingers needs just a side of cooked greens. Add a pinch of cayenne to the cornmeal coating and serve with hot pepper sauce if you like your fish extra spicy.

1. Arrange the racks to divide the oven into thirds. Preheat the oven to 400°F. Spray 2 baking sheets with canola oil nonstick spray.

2. Cut the potatoes into 2 x ½-inch sticks; rinse under cold water and pat dry with paper towels. Spread in a single layer on one of the baking sheets, and spray with canola oil nonstick spray. Bake on the top shelf until golden brown and crisp, about 30 minutes. Season the potatoes with ¼ teaspoon of the salt and ¼ teaspoon of the pepper.

3. Meanwhile, lightly beat the egg in a shallow bowl. On a sheet of wax paper, combine the cornmeal, parsley, the remaining ½ teaspoon salt and ¼ teaspoon pepper. Dip the catfish in the egg, then in the cornmeal mixture, pressing gently to coat. Place on the second baking sheet and spray lightly with the nonstick spray. Bake on the bottom shelf until golden brown and just opaque in the center, 10–15 minutes. Serve with the potatoes and lemon.

PER SERVING (1 FILLET AND ABOUT 1 CUP POTATOES): 328 Cal, 12 g Fat, 3 g Sat Fat, 0 g Trans Fat, 126 mg Chol, 549 mg Sod, 27 g Carb, 4 g Fib, 27 g Prot, 31 mg Calc. **POINTS** value: **7.**

★

★ **tip** If it looks like the potatoes are browning too much on top or the fish is browning too much on the bottom, switch the baking sheets from top to bottom halfway through the baking time.

MAKES 4 SERVINGS

1¼ pounds **red potatoes,** scrubbed

¾ teaspoon **salt**

½ teaspoon freshly **ground pepper**

1 large **egg**

¼ cup **cornmeal**

2 tablespoons finely chopped **fresh parsley**

4 (5-ounce) skinless **catfish fillets**

4 **lemon** wedges

Cod and Vegetable Stew

Cod is a great fish to choose for stew. Its delicate, mild flavor won't overwhelm the other ingredients, and when cooked it breaks into large flakes that will stand up to the chunky vegetables.

1. Combine the potatoes, onions, celery, bell pepper, garlic, thyme, salt, and bay leaf with the water in a large saucepan; bring to a boil. Reduce the heat and simmer, covered, until the potatoes are just tender, 15–20 minutes. Transfer 2 cups of the vegetables and about 1 cup of the cooking liquid to a food processor or blender, and puree.

2. Return the puree to the saucepan and bring to a simmer. Add the cod and cook until just opaque in the center, 3–4 minutes. Gently stir in the parsley, lemon juice, and pepper; discard the bay leaf.

PER SERVING (2 CUPS): 281 Cal, 1 g Fat, 0 g Sat Fat, 0 g Trans Fat, 61 mg Chol, 399 mg Sod, 38 g Carb, 5 g Fib, 30 g Prot, 90 mg Calc. *POINTS* value: *5*.

★

★ **tip** Some fishmongers may sell scrod, which is actually young cod and weighs less than 2½ pounds.

MAKES 4 SERVINGS

- 4 medium **all-purpose potatoes**, peeled and cut into chunks
- 3 **onions**, finely chopped
- 2 **celery** stalks, diced
- 1 **red bell pepper**, seeded and finely chopped
- 3 **garlic cloves**, minced
- 1 teaspoon **dried thyme**
- ½ teaspoon **salt**
- 1 **bay leaf**
- 4 cups **water**
- 1¼ pounds skinless **cod fillets**, cut into 2-inch chunks
- ¼ cup chopped **fresh parsley**
- 2 tablespoons **fresh lemon juice**
- ½ teaspoon freshly **ground pepper**

Grilled Swordfish Steaks with Orange-Lemon Relish

The firm, meaty texture of swordfish makes it a perfect candidate for grilling. For this recipe, the fish is marinated in mustard, olive oil, and garlic, then grilled until smoky and juicy, making a perfect pairing with the tangy citrus relish.

1. Combine the mustard, oil, garlic, and oregano in a zip-close plastic bag; add the swordfish. Squeeze out the air and seal the bag; turn to coat the swordfish. Refrigerate, turning the bag occasionally, at least 1 hour or up to 8 hours.

2. Meanwhile, to make the relish, combine the oranges, scallions, lemon, mint, ¼ teaspoon of the salt, and ⅛ teaspoon of the pepper in a medium bowl. Refrigerate until ready to use.

3. Spray the grill rack with olive oil nonstick spray; prepare the grill.

4. Remove the swordfish from the marinade; discard the marinade. Sprinkle the swordfish with the remaining ½ teaspoon salt and ⅛ teaspoon pepper. Place the swordfish on the grill rack and close the grill. Grill, turning once, until the fish is just opaque in the center, 12–14 minutes. Serve with the relish.

PER SERVING (1 SWORDFISH STEAK WITH ¼ CUP RELISH): 255 Cal, 8 g Fat, 2 g Sat Fat, 0 g Trans Fat, 62 mg Chol, 652 mg Sod, 13 g Carb, 3 g Fib, 33 g Prot, 64 mg Calc.
POINTS value: **5.**

★

★ **tip** To section an orange, cut off the top and bottom of the fruit so that the pulp is exposed. Cut away the peel in strips close to the pulp from top to bottom, using the edge of each previous cut as the starting point for the next cut. Cut along one of the membranes down to the center. Repeat, cutting along the membrane on the other side of the section, which will become free. Repeat with the remaining sections.

MAKES 4 SERVINGS

3 tablespoons **Dijon mustard**

1 tablespoon **olive oil**

2 **garlic cloves**, minced

2 teaspoons **dried oregano**

4 (6-ounce) **swordfish steaks**, about 1-inch thick

2 large navel **oranges**, peeled, cut into sections, and chopped

2 **scallions**, chopped

1 **lemon**, peeled, cut into sections, and chopped

1 tablespoon chopped **fresh mint**

¾ teaspoon **salt**

¼ teaspoon freshly **ground pepper**

Sicilian-Style Halibut

Halibut gets a Mediterranean flavor when baked in this zesty tomato sauce with capers, olives, and herbs. Halibut is a lean fish that dries out easily when overcooked, so be sure to bake it *just* until it loses its glossy appearance and becomes opaque.

1. Preheat the oven to 450°F. Place the halibut in an 8-inch-square baking dish.

2. Spray a large nonstick skillet with olive oil nonstick spray and set over medium-high heat. Add the onion and garlic; cook, stirring frequently, until slightly softened, about 3 minutes. Stir in the tomatoes, capers, olives, lemon juice, basil, oregano, and pepper; bring to a boil. Reduce the heat and simmer, stirring occasionally, until slightly thickened, about 6 minutes. Spoon the sauce over the fish. Bake until the fish is just opaque in the center, about 10 minutes.

PER SERVING (¼ OF HALIBUT AND ABOUT ½ CUP SAUCE): 181 Cal, 3 g Fat, 0 g Sat Fat, 0 g Trans Fat, 35 mg Chol, 463 mg Sod, 14 g Carb, 4 g Fib, 26 g Prot, 97 mg Calc. *POINTS* value: *3.*

MAKES 4 SERVINGS

1 pound skinless **halibut steaks**

1 **onion**, sliced

1 **garlic clove**, minced

2 (14½-ounce) cans diced **tomatoes**

1 tablespoon drained rinsed **capers**

5 **kalamata olives**, pitted and chopped

1 tablespoon **fresh lemon juice**

1 teaspoon **dried basil**

1 teaspoon **dried oregano**

¼ teaspoon freshly **ground pepper**

Sicilian-Style Halibut

Grilled Spiced Shrimp with Papaya Salsa

Shrimp get a quick toss with paprika, thyme, and cayenne, then they're grilled in a flash and served with cooling papaya-lime salsa. If you prefer broiling, thread 4 to 5 shrimp on each of 4 metal skewers.

1. Spray a grill basket or the broiler rack with canola oil nonstick spray; prepare the grill or preheat the broiler. Combine the paprika, thyme, salt, pepper, and cayenne in a zip-close plastic bag; add the shrimp. Squeeze out the air and seal the bag; shake to coat the shrimp.

2. Meanwhile, combine the papaya, scallions, and lime in a small bowl; set aside.

3. Grill the shrimp in the basket or broil the shrimp 6 inches from the heat until just opaque in the center, about 3 minutes on each side. Serve with the salsa on the side.

PER SERVING (ABOUT 4-5 SHRIMP AND SCANT ¾ CUP SALSA): 150 Cal, 1 g Fat, 0 g Sat Fat, 0 g Trans Fat, 221 mg Chol, 531 mg Sod, 10 g Carb, 1 g Fib, 25 g Prot, 79 mg Calc. *POINTS* value: **3.**

★

★ **tip** We keep the tails on the shrimp when shelling, mostly for the sake of presentation, but it's not mandatory. When shelling shrimp, it's always easiest to start at the large end.

MAKES 4 SERVINGS

1½ teaspoons **paprika**

½ teaspoon **dried thyme**

½ teaspoon **salt**

½ teaspoon freshly **ground pepper**

⅛–¼ teaspoon **cayenne**

1¼ pounds large **shrimp**, peeled (tails left on) and deveined

2 cups cubed **papaya**

3 **scallions**, thinly sliced

1 **lime**, peeled and diced

California Rolls

It's fun to make these easy and delicious sushi rolls. You can find nori (sheets of pressed seaweed) and wasabi (Japanese horseradish) in the specialty-foods section of your supermarket or in an Asian grocery.

1. Place 1 sheet of nori on a work surface with the longer side facing you. Lightly moisten with a damp cloth. Spread ½ teaspoon of the wasabi across half of the nori. Moisten your hands and spread ¼ cup of the rice over all but the top 2 inches of the nori. Arrange ¼ cup crabmeat and ¼ cup avocado on top of it. Roll up the bottom of the nori until the ends meet, sealing it. With a serrated knife, using a sawing motion, cut into 6 pieces. Repeat with the remaining nori, 1½ teaspoons of the wasabi, the rice, crabmeat, and avocado, to make 24 pieces.

2. Combine the soy sauce and the remaining 2 teaspoons wasabi in a small bowl; serve with the rolls.

PER SERVING (6 PIECES WITH 1 TABLESPOON SAUCE): 171 Cal, 7 g Fat, 1 g Sat Fat, 0 g Trans Fat, 30 mg Chol, 795 mg Sod, 9 g Carb, 3 g Fib, 9 g Prot, 42 mg Calc. *POINTS* value: **3.**

★

★ **tip** Cook the rice an hour or two before you need it, then cover and let stand at room temperature. Don't refrigerate it, as refrigeration will dry it out.

MAKES 4 SERVINGS

- 4 sheets **nori**

- 4 teaspoons **wasabi paste**

- 1 cup cooked short-grain **brown rice**

- 1 cup cooked lump **crabmeat**, picked over and diced

- 1 cup diced **avocado**

- ¼ cup reduced-sodium **soy sauce**

Ginger-Shrimp and
Green-Bean Stir-Fry

Ginger-Shrimp
and Green-Bean Stir-Fry

This lively stir-fry, with refreshing chunks of pineapple, crisp-tender green beans, and teriyaki sauce, is not spicy, so it's a good choice for the whole family.

1. Heat a large nonstick skillet or wok over medium-high heat until a drop of water sizzles. Pour in 2 teaspoons of the oil, swirl to coat the pan, then add the shrimp. Stir-fry until just opaque in the center, about 3 minutes. Transfer to a plate.

2. Add the remaining 2 teaspoons oil to the skillet. Add the garlic and ginger; stir-fry until fragrant, about 30 seconds. Add the green beans and stir-fry, about 3 minutes. Add the pineapple and stir-fry, about 1 minute. Add the shrimp, broth, teriyaki sauce, and salt; cook, stirring occasionally, until the shrimp are heated through and the green beans are crisp-tender, about 2 minutes. Remove the skillet from the heat and stir in the scallions.

PER SERVING (1 CUP): 224 Cal, 6 g Fat, 1 g Sat Fat, 0 g Trans Fat, 252 mg Chol, 653 mg Sod, 12 g Carb, 2 g Fib, 29 g Prot, 89 mg Calc. *POINTS* value: *5.*

★

★ **tip** Serve over whole-wheat linguine (⅔ cup for each serving will increase the *POINTS* value by 2).

MAKES 4 SERVINGS 🐚 🕐

4 teaspoons **canola oil**

1½ pounds peeled and deveined large **shrimp**

4 **garlic cloves**, minced

1½ tablespoons minced peeled **fresh ginger**

½ pound fresh **green beans**, trimmed

1 (8-ounce) can **pineapple chunks** in juice, drained

⅓ cup reduced-sodium **chicken broth**

2 tablespoons reduced-sodium **teriyaki sauce**

¼ teaspoon **salt**

3 **scallions**, chopped

Scallops with Oranges and Rosemary

Colorful and fresh tasting, this simple preparation for scallops looks like something from a posh restaurant. The scallops are served on a bed of mesclun greens—or you can use shredded romaine lettuce, baby spinach, or arugula.

1. From 1 or 2 of the oranges, remove 5 (3-inch) strips of orange zest with a vegetable peeler. Slice 2 of the strips into the thinnest, longest strips possible. Leave the 3 remaining strips whole.

2. Remove the peel and the pith from the oranges. With a small knife, remove the sections over a bowl.

3. Heat the oil in a large nonstick skillet over medium-high heat. Add the rosemary sprigs and the 3 whole strips of orange zest; cook, stirring frequently, until fragrant, about 1 minute. Add one-third of the scallops (about 8) and cook, turning with tongs, until golden brown, about 2 minutes on each side. Transfer to a medium bowl. Repeat two more times with the remaining scallops.

4. Add the onion and garlic to the skillet and cook, stirring occasionally, until softened, about 2 minutes. Increase the heat to high; add half of the orange sections, any liquid from the cooked scallops, the vinegar, salt, and pepper. Cook, stirring occasionally, about 2 minutes. Discard the orange zest and rosemary sprigs. Return the scallops to the skillet and cook, stirring frequently, until heated through, 1–2 minutes.

5. Arrange the greens on 4 plates and top with the remaining orange sections. Spoon the scallops and sauce over the oranges. Garnish with the thin strips of orange zest and fresh rosemary sprigs.

PER SERVING (1 ½ CUPS GREENS WITH ABOUT 6 SCALLOPS AND ABOUT 1 CUP ORANGE SECTIONS): 296 Cal, 5 g Fat, 1 g Sat Fat, 0 g Trans Fat, 84 mg Chol, 564 mg Sod, 23 g Carb, 5 g Fib, 36 g Prot, 135 mg Calc. *POINTS* value: **6.**

MAKES 4 SERVINGS

4 navel **oranges**

1 tablespoon **olive oil**

2 sprigs **fresh rosemary**

1 ½ pounds **sea scallops**, patted dry on paper towels

1 small **red onion**, thinly sliced

1 **garlic clove**, thinly sliced

1 ½ teaspoons **balsamic vinegar**

¼ teaspoon **salt**

¼ teaspoon freshly **ground pepper**

6 cups mesclun **salad greens**

Fresh rosemary sprigs, for garnish

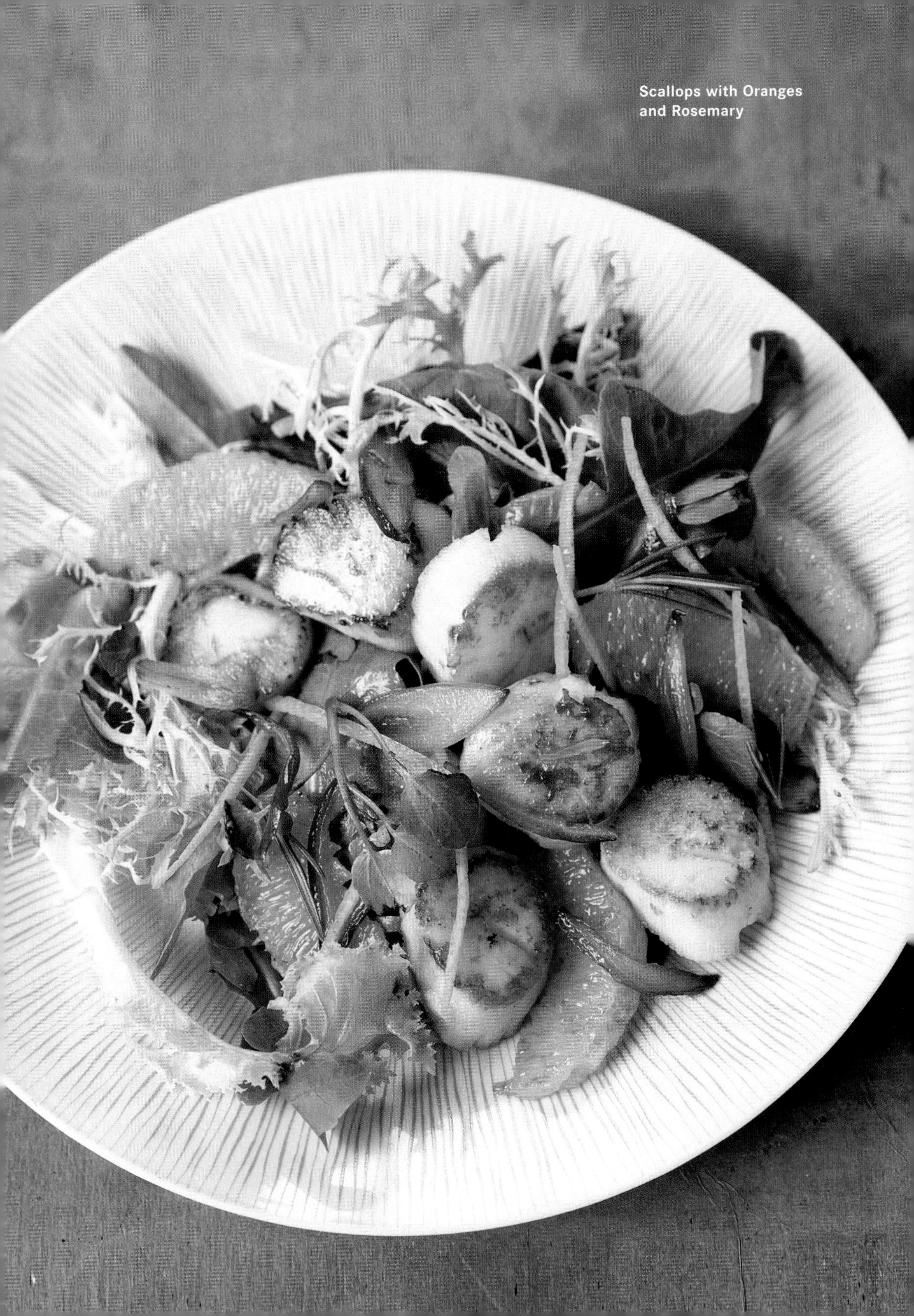

Scallops with Oranges and Rosemary

Tofu-Vegetable Lo Mein

One-bowl dinners like this couldn't be easier to make and more satisfying to serve on nights when you want to skip the meat. This Chinese-inspired favorite boasts four kinds of vegetables, whole-wheat pasta, and silky tofu, all in a light broth with a touch of soy sauce and orange.

1. Combine the broth, orange zest, chopped orange, and soy sauce in a small bowl; set aside.

2. Cook the spaghetti according to package directions; drain.

3. Heat a large nonstick skillet or wok over medium-high heat until a drop of water sizzles. Pour in 1 teaspoon of the oil, swirl to coat the pan, then add the tofu. Stir-fry until lightly golden, 4–5 minutes. Transfer to a plate.

4. Add the remaining 2 teaspoons oil to the skillet. Add the mushrooms and garlic; stir-fry until the mushrooms begin to soften, about 3 minutes. Add the asparagus and carrots; stir-fry until the vegetables begin to soften, 2–3 minutes. Add the tofu and the broth mixture and cook, stirring occasionally, until heated through, about 1 minute. Add the spaghetti and cook, tossing, until well mixed and heated through, 1–2 minutes. Remove the skillet from the heat and stir in the scallions.

PER SERVING (1 CUP): 191 Cal, 4 g Fat, 0 g Sat Fat, 0 g Trans Fat, 0 mg Chol, 386 mg Sod, 30 g Carb, 6 g Fib, 12 g Prot, 53 mg Calc. **POINTS** value: **3.**

MAKES 8 SERVINGS

½ cup **vegetable broth**

½ teaspoon orange zest + ½ navel **orange**, peeled and chopped

¼ cup reduced-sodium **soy sauce**

½ pound **whole-wheat spaghetti**

3 teaspoons **canola oil**

1 (14-ounce) container reduced-fat firm **tofu**, drained and cut into ½-inch cubes

1 (8-ounce) package sliced fresh **mushrooms**

3 **garlic cloves**, minced

1 pound fresh **asparagus**, trimmed and cut into 1½-inch pieces

2 **carrots**, thinly sliced on a diagonal

6 **scallions**, chopped

Vegetable Picadillo

Picadillo is a classic dish in Spanish-speaking countries; it usually includes meat, but this vegetarian version packs as much flavor as the original. Use leftovers as a flavorful filling for baked acorn-squash halves.

Heat the oil in a large nonstick saucepan over medium-high heat. Add the bell peppers, onion, and garlic; cook, stirring frequently, until softened, about 5 minutes. Stir in the beans, tomatoes, tomato paste, cumin, and cayenne; bring to a boil. Reduce the heat and simmer, stirring occasionally, until the flavors are blended, about 20 minutes.

PER SERVING (ABOUT 1 ¼ CUPS): 204 Cal, 3 g Fat, 0 g Sat Fat, 0 g Trans Fat, 0 mg Chol, 321 mg Sod, 36 g Carb, 13 g Fib, 10 g Prot, 80 mg Calc. *POINTS* value: *4.*

★

★ **tip** Some picadillo recipes include raisins, which lend a pleasant sweetness to the dish. If you use ½ cup of raisins (add them with the tomatoes), you'll be increasing the per-serving *POINTS* value by 1.

MAKES 4 SERVINGS 🥕🥕

2 teaspoons **olive oil**

1 **green bell pepper**, seeded and chopped

1 **red bell pepper**, seeded and chopped

1 **onion**, chopped

2 **garlic cloves**, chopped

2 (15-ounce) cans **red kidney beans**, rinsed and drained

1 (14½ -ounce) can diced **tomatoes**

2 tablespoons **tomato paste**

1 teaspoon ground **cumin**

¼ teaspoon **cayenne**

Penne with Roasted Tofu and Vegetables

5 POINTS VALUE

Penne with Roasted Tofu and Vegetables

The narrow, straight Japanese eggplants are worth seeking out for this recipe. Their color ranges from solid purple to striated shades, and they have a tender, slightly sweet flesh. Roasting brings out the naturally sweet, rich flavor of eggplants—and other vegetables. Experiment with different combinations—carrots, yellow squash, red bell pepper, and rosemary are a tasty combination as well.

1. Preheat the oven to 425°F. Combine the tofu, eggplants, fennel, mushrooms, bell pepper, onion, garlic, oil, basil, salt, and pepper in a large roasting pan. Bake, uncovered, until the vegetables are tender, about 40 minutes, tossing every 10 minutes.

2. Meanwhile, cook the penne according to package directions. Drain and toss with the tofu-vegetable mixture in a large serving bowl.

PER SERVING (ABOUT 1 ½ CUPS): 272 Cal, 4 g Fat, 1 g Sat Fat, 0 g Trans Fat, 0 mg Chol, 248 mg Sod, 52 g Carb, 8 g Fib, 13 g Prot, 75 mg Calc. **POINTS** value: **5.**

★

★ **tip** If you like, toss 6 tablespoons of grated Parmesan cheese with the pasta and vegetables in step 2, and increase the per-serving **POINTS** value by 1.

MAKES 6 SERVINGS

1 ½ cups cubed reduced-fat firm **tofu**

1 pound **Japanese eggplants** (about 5), cubed

1 small (about ½ pound) **fennel bulb**, sliced

½ pound fresh **mushrooms**, sliced

1 **red bell pepper**, seeded and cut into 1-inch pieces

1 **sweet onion**, sliced

6 **garlic cloves**, peeled

1 tablespoon **olive oil**

2 teaspoons **dried basil**, crumbled

½ teaspoon **salt**

¼ teaspoon freshly **ground pepper**

3 cups **whole-wheat penne**

Hearty Vegetarian Stew

Two kinds of beans, tofu, and plenty of veggies make this a satisfying meal in a bowl—whether you're an occasional or a full-time vegetarian. We use canned red kidney and white beans, but you can also use black beans, pinto beans, pink beans, or chickpeas.

1. Heat the oil in a large saucepan over medium heat. Add the celery, carrot, onion, and garlic; cook, stirring occasionally, until softened, about 10 minutes.

2. Stir in the tomatoes, kidney beans, white beans, and broth; bring to a boil. Reduce the heat and simmer, covered, stirring occasionally, until the flavors are blended, about 30 minutes. Add the tofu, cilantro, salt, and pepper; cook, stirring occasionally, until the tofu is heated through, about 5 minutes.

PER SERVING (ABOUT 1½ CUPS): 196 Cal, 3 g Fat, 0 g Sat Fat, 0 g Trans Fat, 0 mg Chol, 725 mg Sod, 32 g Carb, 10 g Fib, 11 g Prot, 103 mg Calc. **POINTS** value: **3.**

MAKES 4 SERVINGS

2 teaspoons **olive oil**

2 **celery** stalks, sliced

1 **carrot**, sliced

1 **onion**, chopped

3 **garlic cloves**, minced

1 (14½-ounce) can diced **tomatoes**

1 cup canned **red kidney beans**, rinsed and drained

1 cup canned small **white beans**, rinsed and drained

½ cup reduced-sodium **vegetable broth**

1¼ cups diced reduced-fat firm **tofu**

1 tablespoon chopped **fresh cilantro**

½ teaspoon **salt**

¼ teaspoon freshly **ground pepper**

Lentil-Basmati Pilaf

Look for brown basmati rice and canned lentils in natural foods stores and some supermarkets. If you can't find them, use long-grain brown rice and a can of black beans.

1. Heat the oil in a large nonstick saucepan over medium heat. Add the onion and garlic; cook, stirring occasionally, until softened, about 5 minutes. Stir in the curry powder and cook, stirring constantly, until fragrant, about 30 seconds. Add the rice and cook, stirring to coat, about 1 minute. Stir in the broth, bay leaves, cinnamon stick, and cloves; bring to a boil. Reduce the heat and simmer, covered, until the rice is almost tender, 30–35 minutes.

2. Stir in the lentils, salt, and pepper; cook until the lentils are heated through, about 5 minutes. Discard the bay leaves, cinnamon stick, and cloves. Sprinkle with the parsley.

PER SERVING (ABOUT 1 CUP): 318 Cal, 5 g Fat, 1 g Sat Fat, 0 g Trans Fat, 0 mg Chol, 812 mg Sod, 62 g Carb, 9 g Fib, 10 g Prot, 50 mg Calc. **POINTS** value: **6.**

★

★ **tip** Serve this fragrant pilaf with a dollop of plain fat-free yogurt and chopped fresh cilantro. If you want to bump up the heat, add a good pinch of cayenne with the curry powder or use hot curry powder.

MAKES 4 SERVINGS

2 teaspoons **olive oil**

1 **onion**, chopped

2 **garlic cloves**, minced

1 teaspoon **curry powder**

1 1/3 cups **brown basmati rice**

3 1/2 cups reduced-sodium **vegetable broth**

2 **bay leaves**

1 (4-inch) **cinnamon stick**

2 whole **cloves**

1 (15-ounce) can **lentils,** rinsed and drained

1/2 teaspoon **salt**

1/4 teaspoon freshly **ground pepper**

2 tablespoons chopped **fresh parsley**

Veggie Stuffed Peppers

While red bell peppers are a bit more expensive than their green counterparts, they contain about 10 times more vitamin A, plus their flavor is milder and sweeter. Choose round, evenly shaped peppers that are all about the same size.

1. Preheat the oven to 375°F. In a large pot of boiling water, cook the bell peppers until tender, about 4 minutes, then drain.

2. To prepare the filling, spray a large nonstick skillet with olive oil nonstick spray and set over medium heat. Add the onion and garlic; cook, stirring frequently, until softened, about 5 minutes. Stir in the tomatoes, corn, chili powder, salt, and pepper; bring to a boil. Reduce the heat and simmer, stirring occasionally, until the flavors are blended, about 10 minutes. Stir in the rice.

3. Stuff the filling into each bell-pepper half. Place the stuffed peppers in a shallow 2-quart casserole. Cover with foil and bake until heated through, 20–25 minutes.

PER SERVING (2 BELL-PEPPER HALVES): 157 Cal, 1 g Fat, 0 g Sat Fat, 0 g Trans Fat, 0 mg Chol, 432 mg Sod, 35 g Carb, 7 g Fib, 5 g Prot, 46 mg Calc. *POINTS* value: *2*.

MAKES 4 SERVINGS

- 4 **red bell peppers,** halved and seeded

- 1 **onion**, chopped

- 2 **garlic cloves**, minced

- 1 (14½-ounce) can diced **tomatoes**

- ½ (10-ounce) box frozen **corn kernels**, thawed

- ½ teaspoon **chili powder**

- ½ teaspoon **salt**

- ¼ teaspoon freshly **ground pepper**

- 1 cup cooked **brown rice**

Veggie Stuffed Peppers

CHAPTER 5

Veggies on the Side

Guacamole with a Twist

Though it's as creamy and tasty as restaurant guacamole, no one will ever guess there are canned white beans here to lighten the otherwise high-fat content of the avocado. You can serve this as a side dish or as an appetizer with crudités.

1. Combine the onion and lime juice in a small bowl; let stand 15 minutes.

2. Puree the beans and avocado in a food processor. Add the tomato, cilantro, garlic, salt, hot pepper sauce, cumin, and the onion mixture; pulse until blended. Transfer to a serving dish and serve at once.

PER SERVING (ABOUT $\frac{1}{3}$ CUP): 112 Cal, 5 g Fat, 1 g Sat Fat, 0 g Trans Fat, 0 mg Chol, 281 mg Sod, 15 g Carb, 6 g Fib, 4 g Prot, 28 mg Calc. *POINTS* value: *2*

★

★ **tip** The two most common varieties of avocado are the pebbly-textured, almost-black Haas and the green, smooth- and thin-skinned Fuerte. The Haas has a smaller pit and a more buttery texture than the Fuerte. While both can be used in this recipe, we prefer the Haas avocado.

MAKES 6 SERVINGS

½ **red onion**, minced

3 tablespoons **fresh lime juice**

1 (15-ounce) can **white beans**, rinsed and drained

1 medium **avocado**, peeled and chopped

1 **plum tomato**, finely diced

2 tablespoons chopped **fresh cilantro**

1 **garlic clove**, minced

½ teaspoon **salt**

¼–½ teaspoon **hot pepper sauce**

¼ teaspoon ground **cumin**

Roasted Asparagus with Red Peppers and Lemon

Once you try roasting asparagus, you'll never go back to boiling it. Not only is roasting the easiest way to prepare the vegetable, but it's also the best way to bring out its natural sweetness.

1. Preheat the oven to 400°F. Spray a nonstick baking sheet with olive oil nonstick spray.

2. Combine the asparagus and strips of bell pepper in a large bowl; spray with the nonstick spray. Add the lemon juice, oil, salt, and crushed red pepper; toss well to coat.

3. Arrange the vegetables on the baking sheet in a single layer. Bake until tender, shaking the pan occasionally, 15–18 minutes. Transfer the vegetables to a bowl and toss with the lemon zest.

PER SERVING (ABOUT 3 ASPARAGUS SPEARS AND ¼ CUP BELL-PEPPER STRIPS): 39 Cal, 2 g Fat, 0 g Sat Fat, 0 g Trans Fat, 0 mg Chol, 295 mg Sod, 5 g Carb, 2 g Fib, 2 g Prot, 16 mg Calc. *POINTS* value: *1*.

★

★ **tip** Peak season for asparagus is March through June. Select spears that are fresh and firm with compact tips. They should be straight and round and should snap easily when bent. Contrary to popular belief, spears with larger diameters are just as tender as slender spears.

MAKES 4 SERVINGS

- 1 pound fresh **asparagus,** trimmed

- 1 large **red bell pepper,** seeded and cut into ½-inch strips

- 1 tablespoon **fresh lemon juice**

- 1 teaspoon **olive oil**

- ½ teaspoon **salt**

- ¼ teaspoon **crushed red pepper**

- 1 teaspoon grated **lemon zest**

Cheesy Broccoli and Peppers

Chances are if you just add cheese, the whole family will eat their vegetables. To steam the broccoli, put it in a steamer basket and set in a saucepan over 1 inch of boiling water. Cover tightly and steam until the broccoli is crisp-tender, about 3 minutes.

Heat the oil in a large nonstick skillet over medium-high heat. Add the broccoli, garlic, and oregano; cook, stirring frequently, until the garlic is golden, about 3 minutes. Stir in the cheese and roasted pepper; cook, stirring frequently, until heated through, about 2 minutes.

PER SERVING (ABOUT ¾ CUP): 78 Cal, 3 g Fat, 0 g Sat Fat, 0 g Trans Fat, 3 mg Chol, 192 mg Sod, 8 g Carb, 3 g Fib, 8 g Prot, 182 mg Calc. **POINTS** value: *1.*

★

★ **tip** If there are no kids around and you want to skip the cheddar, you'll reduce the per-serving **POINTS** value by ½ .

MAKES 4 SERVINGS ▰ ◷ ⚴

2 teaspoons **olive oil**

1 pound **broccoli,** chopped and steamed

3 **garlic cloves,** minced

¼ teaspoon **dried oregano,** crumbled

½ cup shredded **fat-free** sharp **cheddar cheese**

¼ cup matchstick-thin strips **roasted red bell pepper**

Broccoli Rabe with Garlic and Fennel

For the more adventurous vegetable fans, broccoli rabe has long been a green of choice. But if you're unfamiliar with its distinct peppery flavor, you're in for a treat. The addition of crushed fennel seeds provides just a touch of sweetness.

1. Bring a large pot of lightly salted water to a boil. Add the broccoli rabe, return to a boil, and cook 2 minutes. Drain and rinse under cold water; then drain again.

2. Heat the oil in a large nonstick skillet over medium-high heat. Add the garlic and fennel seeds; cook, stirring constantly, until fragrant, about 30 seconds. Add the broccoli rabe and cook, tossing occasionally, about 1 minute. Add the broth and salt; bring to a boil. Reduce the heat and simmer, uncovered, until the broccoli rabe is tender, about 3 minutes.

PER SERVING (¾ CUP): 71 Cal, 2 g Fat, 0 g Sat Fat, 0 g Trans Fat, 0 mg Chol, 433 mg Sod, 5 g Carb, 3 g Fib, 5 g Prot, 226 mg Calc. **POINTS** value: **1**.

★

★ **tip** Broccoli rabe, long considered a winter vegetable, is now widely available year-round. Choose broccoli rabe that is bright green with firm, small stems. There should be few buds or open flowers.

MAKES 4 SERVINGS

- 1 bunch **broccoli rabe** (about 1 ½ pounds), trimmed

- 2 teaspoons **extra-virgin olive oil**

- 3 **garlic cloves**, minced

- ¼ teaspoon **fennel seeds**, crushed

- ⅔ cup reduced-sodium **chicken broth**

- ½ teaspoon **salt**

Classic Coleslaw

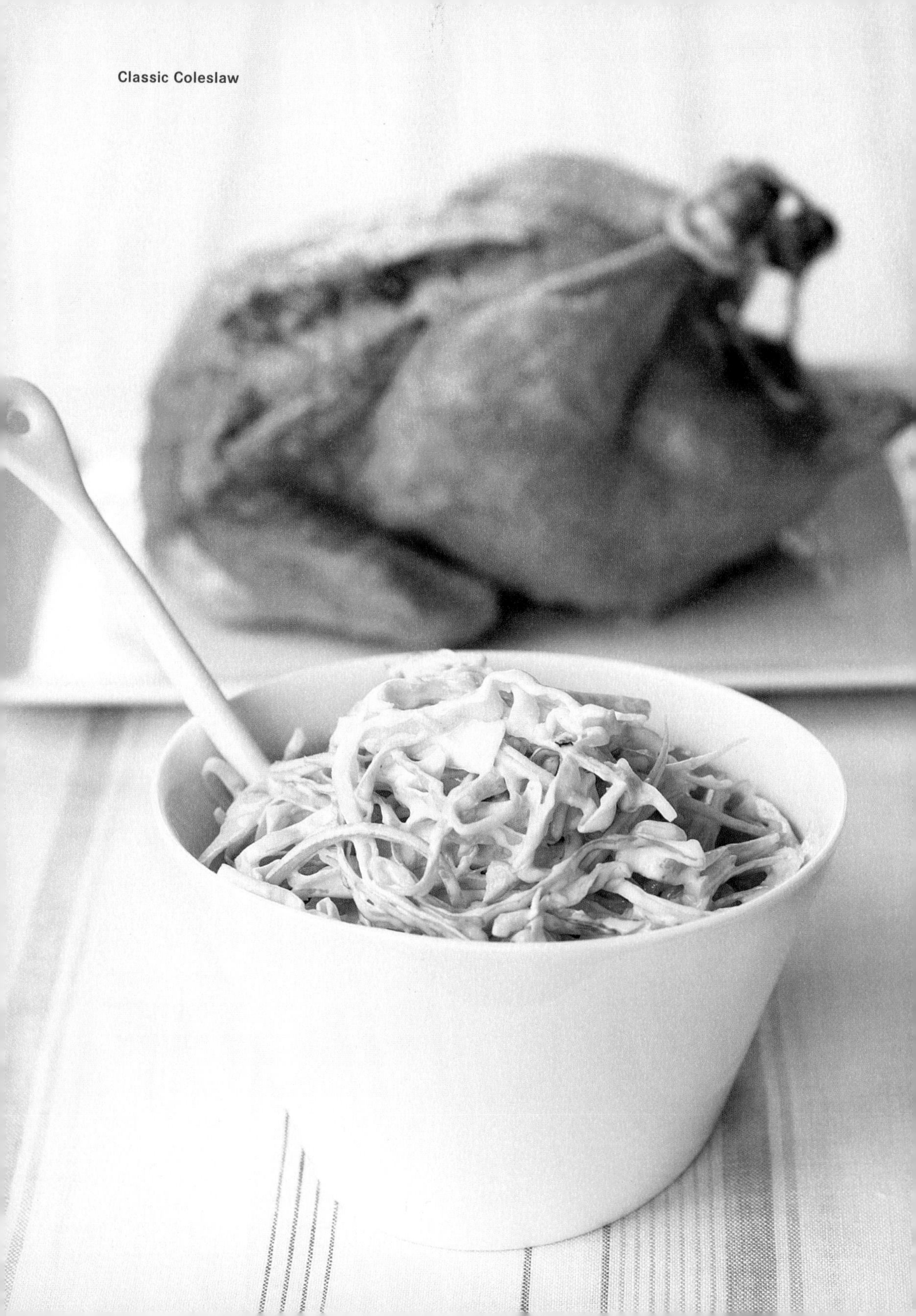

Classic Coleslaw

Immersing the shredded cabbage in cold water makes this coleslaw the crispiest it can be. If you want to add more color, use half red cabbage and half green cabbage. Serve this slaw with roast chicken, if desired.

1. Place the cabbage in a large bowl of cold water; let stand about 1 hour. Drain and dry in a salad spinner, or blot dry with paper towels.

2. Combine the mayonnaise, sour cream, mustard, salt, pepper, and hot pepper sauce in a large bowl. Add the cabbage and carrots; toss to coat. Refrigerate, covered, until ready to serve.

PER SERVING (ABOUT ¾ CUP): 51 Cal, 1 g Fat, 0 g Sat Fat, 0 g Trans Fat, 0 mg Chol, 469 mg Sod, 12 g Carb, 2 g Fib, 1 g Prot, 42 mg Calc. *POINTS* value: *1.*

MAKES 8 SERVINGS

1 head **green cabbage**, shredded

1 cup **fat-free mayonnaise**

1 cup **fat-free sour cream**

2 tablespoons **Dijon mustard**

½ teaspoon **salt**

½ teaspoon freshly **ground pepper**

¼ teaspoon **hot pepper sauce**

2 **carrots**, shredded

Braised Cabbage with Fresh Ginger

This dish is terrific with roast pork tenderloin or grilled pork chops. We prefer red cabbage to green, for the rich burgundy color it gives the dish.

Heat the oil in a medium saucepan over medium-high heat. Add the onion and ginger; cook, stirring frequently, until just fragrant, about 1 minute. Stir in the cabbage and broth. Reduce the heat and simmer, covered, stirring occasionally, until the cabbage is tender, about 20 minutes.

PER SERVING (ABOUT ½ CUP): 53 Cal, 3 g Fat, 0 g Sat Fat, 0 g Trans Fat, 0 mg Chol, 174 mg Sod, 7 g Carb, 2 g Fib, 2 g Prot, 42 mg Calc. *POINTS* value: *1*.

MAKES 4 SERVINGS

2 teaspoons **olive oil**

½ **onion**, thinly sliced

2 tablespoons minced peeled **fresh ginger**

½ small **red cabbage**, thinly sliced (about 4 cups)

⅔ cup **chicken broth**

Red Cabbage and Golden Apple Sauté

This recipe makes a delightful side dish when served with turkey or pork. If you want additional sweetness other than that provided by the apple, stir in 1 tablespoon of honey with the cabbage and increase the vinegar to 2 tablespoons.

Heat the oil in a large nonstick skillet or Dutch oven over medium heat. Add the onion and cook, stirring occasionally, until softened, about 5 minutes. Stir in the cabbage, caraway seeds, and water. Simmer, covered, until the cabbage is barely tender, about 8 minutes. Add the apple, vinegar, salt, and pepper. Simmer, covered, until the cabbage is very tender, about 6 minutes longer.

PER SERVING (ABOUT ⅔ CUP): 64 Cal, 2 g Fat, 0 g Sat Fat, 0 g Trans Fat, 0 mg Chol, 301 mg Sod, 13 g Carb, 3 g Fib, 2 g Prot, 54 mg Calc. **POINTS** value: *1.*

MAKES 4 SERVINGS

1 teaspoon **olive oil**

1 **onion,** sliced

½ small **red cabbage,** sliced (about 5 cups)

½ teaspoon **caraway seeds**

½ cup **water**

1 **Golden Delicious apple,** peeled and diced

1 teaspoon **red-wine vinegar**

½ teaspoon **salt**

¼ teaspoon freshly **ground pepper**

Cauliflower Curry

Steamed cauliflower is topped with a spicy tomato curry and fresh ginger sauce. Don't forget that cauliflower florets are available in convenient packages in the produce aisle of the supermarket. You'll still need to cut them into smaller pieces, but you won't have to hassle with removing the outer leaves and the core.

1. Heat the oil in a large nonstick skillet over medium-high heat. Add the onion and ginger; cook, stirring frequently, until the onion is softened, 4–5 minutes. Stir in the curry powder and cumin; cook, stirring constantly, about 1 minute.

2. Stir in the tomato puree and water. Reduce the heat and simmer, covered, stirring occasionally, about 15 minutes. Remove from the heat and let cool slightly.

3. Place the cauliflower in a serving bowl, top with the sauce, and sprinkle with the parsley.

PER SERVING (ABOUT 1 CUP): 73 Cal, 2 g Fat, 0 g Sat Fat, 0 g Trans Fat, 0 mg Chol, 266 mg Sod, 14 g Carb, 5 g Fib, 3 g Prot, 51 mg Calc. *POINTS* value: *1*.

★

★ **tip** If you want to extend this dish, add 1⅓ cups of canned chickpeas, drained and rinsed to the sauce. (You'll increase the per-serving *POINTS* value by 1.)

MAKES 4 SERVINGS 🥩 🥕

- 1 teaspoon **olive oil**
- 1 **onion**, finely chopped
- 2 teaspoons minced peeled **fresh ginger**
- 2 teaspoons **curry powder**
- ½ teaspoon ground **cumin**
- 1 cup canned **tomato puree**
- 1½ cups **water**
- 1 pound **cauliflower** florets, cut into bite-size pieces and steamed
- 1 tablespoon chopped **fresh parsley**

Zucchini with Orange and Mint

This quick sauté goes particularly well with grilled fish and chicken. Serve it hot or at room temperature.

1. Grate ¼ teaspoon zest from the orange. Then peel and chop the orange and set aside.

2. Spray a large nonstick skillet with olive oil nonstick spray and set over medium-high heat. Add the garlic and cook, stirring constantly, until fragrant, about 30 seconds. Add the zucchini and cook, stirring frequently, until softened, about 5 minutes. Stir in the chopped orange, orange zest, vinegar, and salt; cook until the liquid is slightly thickened but hasn't evaporated, about 2 minutes. Remove from the heat and stir in the mint.

PER SERVING (ABOUT ¾ CUP): 32 Cal, 0 g Fat, 0 g Sat Fat, 0 g Trans Fat, 0 mg Chol, 124 mg Sod, 7 g Carb, 2 g Fib, 2 g Prot, 35 mg Calc. **POINTS** value: *0.*

★

★ **tip** To store fresh mint (and other herbs), place a bunch stem-end down in a glass of water with a plastic bag over the leaves. Refrigerate for up to a week, changing the water every 2 days.

MAKES 4 SERVINGS

- 1 navel **orange**
- 2 **garlic cloves**, minced
- 3 medium **zucchini**, cut into ¼-inch rounds
- 1 tablespoon **red-wine vinegar**
- ¼ teaspoon kosher **salt**
- 3 tablespoons chopped **fresh mint**

Spaghetti-Squash Sauté

Spaghetti squash is a great stand-in for pasta. Its crisp-tender, golden strands have a slightly sweet flavor, making the vegetable perfect to pair with asparagus, peas, and lemon. When selecting spaghetti squash, remember that the larger the vegetable, the thicker the strands—and usually the greater the flavor.

1. Preheat the oven to 350°F. Cut the squash in half lengthwise and scoop out the seeds. Place the squash, cut-side down, in a 7 x 11-inch baking dish; add water to a depth of about 1/2 inch. Cover with foil and bake until tender, about 45 minutes. Remove the squash from the water and let stand until cool enough to handle. With a fork, scrape out the pulp; then transfer it to a medium bowl.

2. Heat the oil in a large nonstick skillet over medium-high heat. Add the scallions and garlic; cook, stirring constantly, until fragrant, about 1 minute. Add the broth, marjoram, lemon zest, and salt; bring to a boil. Add the asparagus and peas, reduce the heat, and simmer, covered, about 2 minutes. Stir in the squash and lemon juice; cook, stirring occasionally, until heated through, about 3 minutes.

PER SERVING (ABOUT 1 CUP): 117 Cal, 4 g Fat, 1 g Sat Fat, 0 g Trans Fat, 0 mg Chol, 328 mg Sod, 19 g Carb, 2 g Fib, 5 g Prot, 63 mg Calc. *POINTS* value: *2.*

★

★ **tip** The spaghetti squash may also be cooked in a microwave. Pierce with a fork, place on a paper towel, and microwave on High until softened, 8–12 minutes, turning it over and rotating a quarter turn every 3 minutes. Let stand 5 minutes. Then cut open, discard the seeds, and scrape the pulp into a bowl.

MAKES 4 SERVINGS

1 (2-pound) **spaghetti squash**

2 teaspoons **olive oil**

2 **scallions**, thinly sliced

2 **garlic** cloves, minced

½ cup **chicken broth**

½ teaspoon **dried marjoram**

½ teaspoon grated **lemon zest**

¼ teaspoon **salt**

12 thin fresh **asparagus** spears, trimmed and cut into 2-inch diagonal lengths

1 cup **frozen peas**, thawed

2 teaspoons **fresh lemon juice**

Spaghetti-Squash Sauté

Zucchini-Tomato Sauté

Zucchini-Tomato Sauté

We use cherry tomatoes in this summery sauté, but you can also use grape tomatoes or a mix of tiny, sweet red and yellow tomatoes. Consider serving this side dish with grilled swordfish steaks, as pictured.

Spray a large nonstick skillet with olive oil nonstick spray and set over medium-high heat. Add the zucchini and garlic; cook, stirring frequently, until the zucchini is crisp-tender, 1–2 minutes. Stir in the tomatoes, salt, and pepper; cook, stirring frequently, until the tomatoes are heated through, about 1 minute. Remove from the heat and stir in the mint.

PER SERVING (ABOUT ¾ CUP): 39 Cal, 1 g Fat, 0 g Sat Fat, 0 g Trans Fat, 0 mg Chol, 158 mg Sod, 8 g Carb, 3 g Fib, 3 g Prot, 33 mg Calc. **POINTS** value: **0.**

★

★ **tip** Stirring in the mint after the skillet has been removed from the heat prevents the mint from turning black. If you have extra mint leaves, use them as a garnish.

MAKES 4 SERVINGS

3 medium **zucchini**, diced

1 **garlic clove**, minced

18 **cherry tomatoes**, halved

¼ teaspoon **salt**

⅛ teaspoon freshly **ground pepper**

2 tablespoons chopped **fresh mint**

Skillet Greens with Garlic and Red Pepper

Dark-green leafy vegetables are full of nutrients, and when simply prepared with garlic and crushed red pepper, they taste delicious. We call for a wide variety of greens in this recipe, so choose whatever looks best at your market. Just keep in mind that the cooking time will depend on which green you're using.

Heat the oil in a large nonstick Dutch oven over medium-high heat. Add the garlic and cook, stirring constantly, until fragrant and lightly browned, about 30 seconds. Stir in the salt and crushed red pepper. Reduce the heat and add the greens, a handful or two at a time, stirring to help them wilt. Add the water to prevent scorching and cook, covered, stirring occasionally, until the greens are tender, about 10 minutes.

PER SERVING (ABOUT ¾ CUP): 56 Cal, 3 g Fat, 0 g Sat Fat, 0 g Trans Fat, 0 mg Chol, 318 mg Sod, 7 g Carb, 2 g Fib, 2 g Prot, 89 mg Calc. *POINTS* value: *1.*

MAKES 4 SERVINGS

- 2 teaspoons **olive oil**
- 2–3 **garlic cloves**, minced
- ½ teaspoon **salt**
- ⅛ teaspoon **crushed red pepper**
- 1 large bunch **cooking greens** (kale, escarole, spinach, Swiss chard, mustard, turnip, or collard greens) cleaned and coarsely chopped
- 2–3 tablespoons **water**

Chili Beans and Corn

This colorful side dish, chock-full of three kinds of beans and bell peppers, can be served in a number of ways. Try it as a side dish with grilled steak, chicken, or fish or as a vegetarian entrée spooned over brown rice or whole-wheat couscous. If you prefer your beans on the milder side, reduce the amount of chili powder by half.

1. Heat the oil in a large nonstick saucepan over medium heat. Add the onion and cook, stirring frequently, about 3 minutes. Add the garlic and cook, stirring constantly, about 1 minute. Add the bell peppers; cook, stirring occasionally, until the vegetables are softened, about 5 minutes. Add the chili powder and cumin; cook, stirring constantly, about 1 minute.

2. Stir in the tomatoes, corn, salt, pepper, and water; bring to a boil. Reduce the heat and simmer until the flavors are blended, about 30 minutes. Add the beans and vinegar; cook until the beans are heated through, about 15 minutes.

PER SERVING (ABOUT 1 CUP): 218 Cal, 3 g Fat, 0 g Sat Fat, 0 g Trans Fat, 0 mg Chol, 449 mg Sod, 41 g Carb, 12 g Fib, 11 g Prot, 95 mg Calc. **POINTS** value: **4.**

MAKES 8 SERVINGS

2 teaspoons **canola oil**

1 large **onion**, chopped

2 **garlic cloves**, chopped

3 **assorted color bell peppers**, seeded and chopped

2 tablespoons **chili powder**

1 teaspoon ground **cumin**

1 (28-ounce) can **crushed tomatoes**

1 (10-ounce) box frozen **corn kernels**, thawed

¼ teaspoon **salt**

¼ teaspoon freshly **ground pepper**

1 cup **water**

1 (19-ounce) can **black beans**, rinsed and drained

1 (19-ounce) can **red kidney beans**, rinsed and drained

1 (19-ounce) can **pinto beans**, rinsed and drained

2 teaspoons **white vinegar**

Succotash

While there are a number of versions of succotash, it wouldn't be authentic without corn or lima beans. What was once considered a summer dish can now be made year-round because both vegetables are available frozen. This dish is great served with juicy grilled pork chops.

1. Heat the oil in a large nonstick skillet over medium heat. Add the bell pepper, zucchini, onion, and garlic; cook, stirring occasionally, until softened, about 8 minutes. Add the tomato and cook, stirring occasionally, about 2 minutes.

2. Stir in the lima beans, corn, parsley, paprika, salt, pepper, and marjoram. Reduce the heat and simmer, covered, until the flavors blend, about 10 minutes.

PER SERVING (ABOUT ¾ CUP): 131 Cal, 3 g Fat, 3 g Sat Fat, 0 g Trans Fat, 0 mg Chol, 309 mg Sod, 23 g Carb, 5 g Fib, 5 g Prot, 35 mg Calc. **POINTS** value: **2.**

★
★ **tip** To remove fresh corn kernels from the cob, begin by cutting a small piece off the tip so that it's flat. Holding the stem end, stand the cob upright on its flat end. Set it on a plate and use a knife to cut downward, removing the corn 3 or 4 rows at a time. You'll need 2 medium-size ears to yield 1 cup of kernels.

MAKES 4 SERVINGS 🍴

2 teaspoons **olive oil**

1 **red bell pepper**, seeded and diced

½ medium **zucchini**, diced

½ **onion**, diced

1 **garlic clove**, finely chopped

1 **tomato**, seeded and diced

1 cup frozen **lima beans**, thawed

1 cup fresh or thawed frozen **corn kernels**

2 tablespoons chopped flat-leaf **parsley**

1 teaspoon **paprika**

½ teaspoon **salt**

½ teaspoon freshly **ground pepper**

¼ teaspoon **dried marjoram**

Succotash

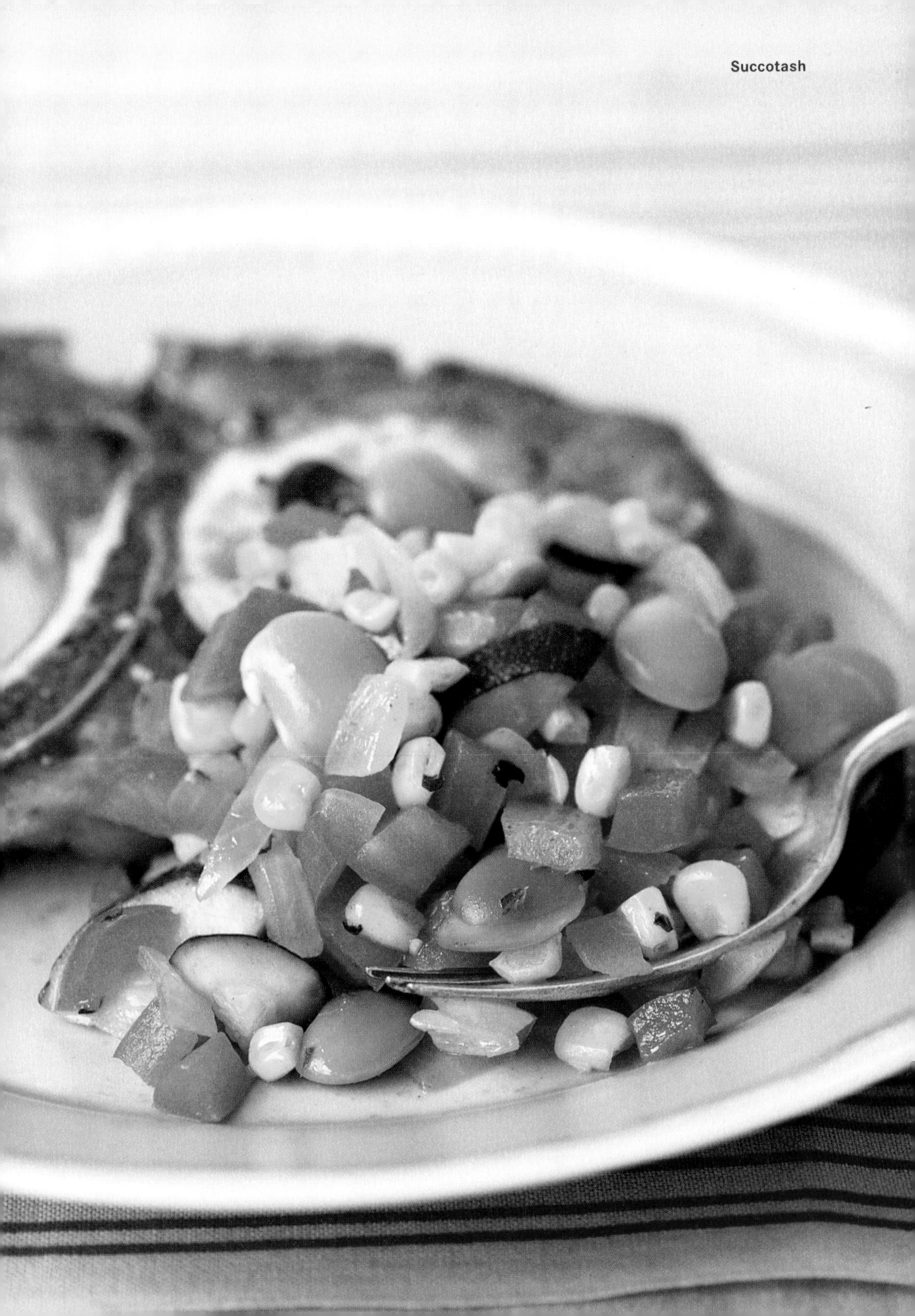

Sour Cream and Garlic Mashed Potatoes

These delicious potatoes only taste indulgent. The trick to keeping the fat grams in check while maintaining the creamy consistency is adding some of the liquid the potatoes cook in, instead of butter, when mashing.

1. Combine the potatoes and garlic in a large saucepan; add enough water to cover. Bring to a boil, reduce the heat, and simmer until the potatoes are tender, 20–30 minutes. Drain, reserving ¾ cup of the cooking liquid.

2. Mash the potatoes and garlic in the saucepan. Stir in the sour cream, oil, salt, and pepper. Gradually stir in enough of the cooking liquid, 2 or 3 tablespoons at a time, until the potatoes become creamy.

PER SERVING (ABOUT ¾ CUP): 158 Cal, 4 g Fat, 0 g Sat Fat, 0 g Trans Fat, 0 mg Chol, 83 mg Sod, 29 g Carb, 2 g Fib, 3 g Prot, 33 mg Calc. *POINTS* value: **3**.

★
★ **tip** Sprinkle the potatoes with 1 tablespoon chopped fresh parsley or snipped fresh chives.

MAKES 4 SERVINGS 🍖 🥕

1 ¼ pounds (about 4) **russet potatoes**, peeled and chopped

5 **garlic cloves**, peeled

3 tablespoons **fat-free sour cream**

1 tablespoon **olive oil**

⅛ teaspoon **salt**

⅛ teaspoon freshly **ground pepper**

Two-Potato Salad

Red and sweet potatoes team up in this creamy salad with a splash of balsamic vinegar. Look for tiny new potatoes, sometimes labeled "baby potatoes," in the supermarket. If you find them, you may need only to cut them in half—or even leave them whole.

1. Combine the red potatoes and sweet potatoes in a large pot; add cold water to cover. Bring to a boil, reduce the heat, and simmer until tender, 15–20 minutes. Drain and rinse under cold water.

2. Combine the vinegar, oil, and garlic in a large bowl. Add the onion and potatoes; toss gently to coat.

3. Combine the parsley, mayonnaise, yogurt, salt, and pepper in a small bowl. Pour over the potatoes and toss to coat. Refrigerate, covered, until the flavors are blended, at least 3 hours.

PER SERVING (ABOUT ½ CUP): 162 Cal, 2 g Fat, 0 g Sat Fat, 0 g Trans Fat, 1 mg Chol, 137 mg Sod, 33 g Carb, 3 g Fib, 3 g Prot, 33 mg Calc. *POINTS* value: *3.*

MAKES 8 SERVINGS

- 1½ pounds small **red potatoes**, scrubbed and quartered

- 1¼ pounds **sweet potatoes**, peeled and cut into chunks

- 1 tablespoon **balsamic vinegar**

- 1 tablespoon **olive oil**

- 1 **garlic clove**, minced

- ½ **red onion**, finely chopped

- ¼ cup chopped **fresh parsley**

- 3 tablespoons **fat-free mayonnaise**

- 3 tablespoons plain **fat-free yogurt**

- ¼ teaspoon **salt**

- ⅛ teaspoon freshly **ground pepper**

Crispy Sweet-Potato "Fries"

These totally addictive baked "fries" are a natural with ketchup, but try them, too, with a little fat-free mayonnaise mixed with a squirt of fresh lime juice.

1. Preheat the oven to 450°F. Halve the potatoes and cut into ½-inch wedges. Toss with the oil, salt, and pepper in a medium bowl.

2. Arrange the potatoes in a single layer on a nonstick baking sheet. Bake, turning once, until browned and crisp, about 35 minutes.

PER SERVING (ABOUT 1 CUP): 234 Cal, 4 g Fat, 0 g Sat Fat, 0 g Trans Fat, 0 mg Chol, 153 mg Sod, 48 g Carb, 6 g Fib, 3 g Prot, 57 mg Calc. *POINTS* value: *4.*

★
★ **tip** Store sweet potatoes in a cool, dark, well-ventilated place for up to 2 weeks.

MAKES 4 SERVINGS

2 pounds large **sweet potatoes**, scrubbed

1 tablespoon **olive oil**

¼ teaspoon **salt**

¼ teaspoon freshly **ground pepper**

Crispy Sweet-Potato "Fries" and Spicy Potato Sticks, page 156

Spicy Potato Sticks

It's hard to believe these crisp oven-baked "fries" are totally fat-free. Omit the pepper if you're using hot chili powder.

Preheat the oven to 425°F. Spray a large nonstick baking sheet with canola oil nonstick spray. Combine all of the ingredients in a large bowl and toss to coat. Transfer to the baking sheet and arrange in a single layer. Bake until the potatoes are barely tender, about 15 minutes. Increase the oven temperature to broil and broil 5 inches from the heat until crispy, about 10 minutes longer.

PER SERVING (ABOUT 1 CUP): 73 Cal, 0 g Fat, 0 g Sat Fat, 0 g Trans Fat, 0 mg Chol, 327 mg Sod, 15 g Carb, 2 g Fib, 3 g Prot, 12 mg Calc. *POINTS* value: *1*.

MAKES 4 SERVINGS

2 large **baking potatoes**, scrubbed and cut into thin strips

2 **egg whites**, lightly beaten

¾ teaspoon ground **cumin**

½ teaspoon **salt**

½ teaspoon **chili powder**

¼ teaspoon freshly **ground pepper** (optional)

Herbed Baked Potatoes

Vary the herbs here if you wish. We use parsley and chives, but 2 teaspoons of chopped fresh rosemary, thyme, or oregano would work quite nicely, too.

1. Preheat the oven to 350°F. Spray a large nonstick baking sheet with olive oil nonstick spray. Combine the potatoes and oil in a large bowl; toss to coat. Transfer to a baking sheet and arrange in a single layer. Bake, turning the potatoes once, until tender and golden, about 1 hour.

2. Meanwhile, spray a medium nonstick skillet with olive oil nonstick spray and set over medium heat. Add the scallions, parsley, and chives; cook, stirring constantly, until fragrant, about 2 minutes. Spoon over the baked potatoes with the salt and pepper; toss to coat.

PER SERVING (ABOUT ¾ CUP): 156 Cal, 3 g Fat, 0 g Sat Fat, 0 g Trans Fat, 0 mg Chol, 207 mg Sod, 30 g Carb, 3 g Fib, 4 g Prot, 18 mg Calc. **POINTS** value: **3.**

★

★ **tip** You can also boil the potatoes for this dish— they'll cook faster. Place the potatoes in a pot, add cold water to cover, and bring to a boil. Reduce the heat and simmer until tender, 15 to 20 minutes. Drain and transfer to a large bowl. Cook the scallions, parsley, and chives as directed in step 2, but use 1 tablespoon olive oil instead of the nonstick spray. Spoon the herbs over the potatoes with the salt and pepper; toss to coat.

MAKES 6 SERVINGS 🥕

2 pounds small **red potatoes**, scrubbed and quartered

1 tablespoon **olive oil**

2 **scallions**, sliced

1 tablespoon chopped **fresh parsley**

1 teaspoon snipped **fresh chives**

½ teaspoon **salt**

⅛ teaspoon freshly **ground pepper**

Ratatouille

Considered a condiment as well as a side dish, ratatouille hails from the sun-drenched region of Provence in France. Eggplant, zucchini, bell pepper, onion, and tomatoes simmer with garlic and fresh basil, then the mixture is served at room temperature. This recipe can easily be doubled. Its flavor only improves with time.

1. Put the eggplant in a colander in the sink and sprinkle with ¾ teaspoon of the salt. Let stand 20 minutes, then rinse under cold water, and pat dry with paper towels.

2. Heat the oil in a large nonstick saucepan over medium-high heat. Add the eggplant, zucchini, bell pepper, onion, and garlic; cook, stirring constantly, about 1 minute; then add the water. Reduce the heat and simmer, covered, shaking the pan occasionally, until the vegetables are softened, about 5 minutes. Stir in the tomatoes, basil, pepper, and the remaining ¼ teaspoon salt; simmer, uncovered, until the liquid is evaporated, about 25 minutes. Disgard the garlic. Let cool to room temperature before serving.

PER SERVING (ABOUT ¾ CUP): 75 Cal, 3 g Fat, 0 g Sat Fat, 0 g Trans Fat, 0 mg Chol, 363 mg Sod, 13 g Carb, 4 g Fib, 2 g Prot, 35 mg Calc. *POINTS* value: *1*.

★

★ **tip** Salting and draining the eggplant extracts the bitter juices, which may affect the flavor of the dish. If you have any ratatouille left over, use it as a pasta sauce or an omelette filling. Ratatouille will keep in the refrigerator in an airtight container for up to 1 week.

MAKES 6 SERVINGS

- 1 small (¾-pound) **eggplant**, chopped
- 1 teaspoon **salt**
- 1 tablespoon **olive oil**
- 2 medium **zucchini**, chopped
- 1 **red bell pepper**, seeded and chopped
- 1 **onion**, chopped
- 2 **garlic cloves**, crushed
- ¼ cup **water**
- 1 (14½-ounce) can diced **tomatoes**
- 2 tablespoons shredded **fresh basil**
- ¼ teaspoon freshly **ground pepper**

Spicy Green-Bean Stir-Fry

This Szechuan-style stir-fry is especially tasty served with boneless pork chops or skinless, boneless chicken breasts. The bamboo shoots are an optional ingredient; you can also add sliced water chestnuts.

1. Put the green beans in a steamer basket and set in a saucepan over 1 inch of boiling water. Cover tightly and steam until crisp-tender, about 5 minutes.

2. Meanwhile, combine the soy sauce, ketchup, vinegar, and hot pepper sauce in a small bowl.

3. Spray a large nonstick skillet with canola oil nonstick spray and set over medium-high heat. Add the green beans and garlic; stir-fry, about 2 minutes. Add the soy-sauce mixture and cook, stirring occasionally, about 1 minute. Stir in the bamboo shoots (if using) and oil.

PER SERVING (ABOUT ¾ CUP): 58 Cal, 2 g Fat, 0 g Sat Fat, 0 g Trans Fat, 0 mg Chol, 351 mg Sod, 10 g Carb, 4 g Fib, 3 g Prot, 53 mg Calc. **POINTS** value: **1**.

MAKES 4 SERVINGS

- 1 pound fresh **green beans**, trimmed and cut into 2-inch pieces

- 2 tablespoons reduced-sodium **soy sauce**

- 2 teaspoons **ketchup**

- 1 teaspoon **red-wine vinegar**

- ½ teaspoon **hot pepper sauce**

- 1 **garlic clove**, minced

- 1 (8-ounce) can sliced **bamboo shoots**, drained (optional)

- 1 teaspoon **canola oil**

Moroccan Carrots and Sugar-Snap Peas

Cumin, curry powder, and lemon juice infuse this easy vegetable dish with great flavor.

1. Bring 1 inch of water to a simmer in a medium skillet. Add the carrots and cook 5 minutes. Add the sugar-snap peas and cook until both vegetables are crisp-tender, about 2 minutes longer. Drain the vegetables in a colander.

2. Heat the oil in the skillet over medium-high heat. Add the cumin and curry powder; cook, stirring constantly, until fragrant, 15–30 seconds. Add the vegetables, lemon juice, and salt; cook, stirring constantly, until heated through, 2–3 minutes.

PER SERVING (ABOUT 1 CUP): 48 Cal, 2 g Fat, 0 g Sat Fat, 0 g Trans Fat, 0 mg Chol, 169 mg Sod, 8 g Carb, 2 g Fib, 1 g Prot, 35 mg Calc. **POINTS** value: **1**.

★

★ **tip** Serve with whole-wheat couscous (⅔ cup cooked couscous will increase the **POINTS** value by 2) and sprinkle with grated lemon or orange zest for extra flavor.

MAKES 4 SERVINGS

- 1 (½-pound) package **baby carrots** (about 2 cups), halved lengthwise

- ¼ pound fresh **sugar-snap peas** (about 1½ cups)

- 1 teaspoon **olive oil**

- 1 teaspoon ground **cumin**

- ½ teaspoon **curry powder**

- 2 teaspoons **fresh lemon juice**

- ¼ teaspoon **salt**

Moroccan Carrots and Sugar-Snap Peas

Easy Roasted Vegetables

For successful roasting, you'll need to use a very hot oven so that the natural sugars in the vegetables caramelize and become intensely flavorful. Grilled steak would pair well with this zesty, spiced dish.

1. Preheat the oven to 450°F. Combine the potatoes and oil in a 9 x 13-inch baking pan. Bake about 15 minutes.

2. Meanwhile, combine the chili powder, cumin, salt, thyme, and pepper in a small bowl. Add to the potatoes. Then add the zucchini, bell peppers, and onion; toss to coat. Bake until the vegetables are tender, about 25 minutes longer.

PER SERVING (ABOUT 1 ¼ CUPS): 102 Cal, 3 g Fat, 0 g Sat Fat, 0 g Trans Fat, 0 mg Chol, 191 mg Sod, 18 g Carb, 4 g Fib, 3 g Prot, 26 mg Calc. *POINTS* value: *1*.

MAKES 6 SERVINGS

1 ¼ pounds **red potatoes**, scrubbed and quartered

1 tablespoon **olive oil**

1 teaspoon **chili powder**

½ teaspoon ground **cumin**

½ teaspoon **salt**

¼ teaspoon **dried thyme**, crumbled

⅛ teaspoon freshly **ground pepper**

3 medium **zucchini**, cut into large chunks

2 **red bell peppers**, seeded and cut into strips

1 **sweet onion**, sliced

POINTS VALUE 1

Mediterranean Vegetable Casserole

A glorious assortment of vegetables are roasted, then layered with fresh herbs and baked until bubbly and golden brown.

1. Heat oven to 400°F. Spray 2 nonstick baking sheets and a 1-quart casserole with nonstick spray.

2. Combine the eggplant and 1 teaspoon of the oil in a bowl. Transfer to a baking sheet and arrange in a single layer. Repeat, first with the squash and then with the zucchini, tossing each vegetable with 1 teaspoon of the oil and arranging in a single layer on the second baking sheet. Bake the vegetables for 12 minutes. Turn the vegetables over and bake 8 minutes. Remove vegetables from the oven and reduce the oven temperature to 350°F.

3. Heat the remaining 1 teaspoon oil in a large nonstick skillet over medium heat. Add the bell pepper, onion, and garlic; cook, stirring frequently, until softened. Cover the skillet and cook, shaking the skillet occasionally, about 5 minutes.

4. Combine the tomato paste and water in a small bowl. Combine the parsley, basil, thyme, salt, and pepper in another small bowl.

5. Arrange half of the eggplant in the casserole and sprinkle with 1 teaspoon of the herbs. Continue layering with half of the tomato, half of the sautéed vegetables, and half of the squash and zucchini, sprinkling 1 teaspoon herbs between each layer. Repeat the layers, ending with the squash and zucchini. Pour the tomato-paste mixture over the top. Cover and bake until the vegetables are tender, 50 minutes. Uncover and bake until browned, about 15 minutes.

PER SERVING (ABOUT ¾ CUP): 80 Cal, 4 g Fat, 0 g Sat Fat, 0 g Trans Fat, 0 mg Chol, 184 mg Sod, 12 g Carb, 3 g Fib, 2 g Prot, 58 mg Calc. **POINTS** value: **1.**

MAKES 6 SERVINGS

- 1 small (about ¾-pound) **eggplant**, peeled and cut into ¼-inch slices

- 4 teaspoons **olive oil**

- 1 large **yellow squash**, cut into ¼-inch diagonal slices

- 1 medium **zucchini**, cut into ¼-inch diagonal slices

- 1 **red bell pepper**, seeded and cut into strips

- 1 **onion**, very thinly sliced

- 3 **garlic cloves**, very thinly sliced

- ¼ cup **tomato paste**

- ½ cup **water**

- 2 tablespoons finely chopped **fresh parsley**

- 2 tablespoons finely chopped **fresh basil**

- 2 teaspoons finely chopped **fresh thyme**

- ¼ teaspoon **salt**

- ¼ teaspoon freshly **ground pepper**

- 1 **tomato**, thinly sliced

Buddha's Delight

Buddha's Delight

This classic vegetable stir-fry is traditionally served on the Chinese New Year. Unlike the take-out variety, this dish cooks the vegetables in just a scant amount of oil.

1. Combine the broth, soy sauce, garlic, and ginger in a small bowl.

2. Heat a large, nonstick skillet or wok over high heat until a drop of water sizzles. Pour in the oil and swirl to coat the pan, then add the bok choy and bell pepper. Stir-fry about 3 minutes; add the broth mixture, snow peas, and carrot. Reduce the heat and cook, stirring frequently, until the vegetables are crisp-tender, about 3 minutes. Stir in the bamboo shoots and water chestnuts; cook, stirring frequently, until heated through, about 1 minute longer.

PER SERVING (ABOUT 1 CUP): 65 Cal, 3 g Fat, 0 g Sat Fat, 0 g Trans Fat, 0 mg Chol, 243 mg Sod, 9 g Carb, 2 g Fib, 3 g Prot, 63 mg Calc. **POINTS** value: **1**.

★

★ **tip** Brown rice would make a nice accompaniment to this dish (½ cup cooked rice for each serving will increase the **POINTS** value by 2).

MAKES 4 SERVINGS

¼ cup **chicken broth**

1 tablespoon reduced-sodium **soy sauce**

2 **garlic cloves**, minced

1½ teaspoons grated peeled **fresh ginger**

2 teaspoons **canola oil**

2 cups chopped **bok choy**

1 **red bell pepper**, seeded and cut into 1-inch squares

1 cup fresh **snow peas**, trimmed

½ **carrot**, thinly sliced on the diagonal

¼ cup canned sliced **bamboo shoots**, drained

¼ cup canned sliced **water chestnuts**, drained

Roasted Root Vegetables

Two kinds of potatoes, carrots, parsnips, beets, and onions make this a hearty side dish for roast chicken or pork. The beets add a sweet flavor to the dish and turn it a vibrant red-pink.

1. Preheat the oven to 400°F. Place the oil in a large shallow roasting pan or jelly-roll pan. Heat the pan in the oven until the oil is hot, about 2 minutes. Add the red potatoes, sweet potato, carrots, parsnips, beets, and onions.

2. Combine the broth, tomato paste, garlic, thyme, salt, and pepper in a small bowl. Pour over the vegetables; mix well. Bake, stirring a few times, until the vegetables are tender, about 45 minutes. Serve hot or warm.

PER SERVING (ABOUT ¾ CUP): 186 Cal, 3 g Fat, 0 g Sat Fat, 0 g Trans Fat, 0 mg Chol, 327 mg Sod, 38 g Carb, 6 g Fib, 4 g Prot, 54 mg Calc. *POINTS* value: **3.**

MAKES 6 SERVINGS

- 1 tablespoon **olive oil**
- ¾ pound small **red potatoes**, scrubbed and quartered
- 1 large **sweet potato**, peeled and cut into ¾-inch chunks
- 4 **carrots**, sliced
- 2 **parsnips**, peeled and sliced
- 2 fresh **beets**, peeled and cut into ¾-inch chunks
- 2 **onions**, cut into ¾-inch chunks
- ½ cup **chicken broth**
- 1 tablespoon **tomato paste**
- 2 **garlic cloves**, crushed
- ½ teaspoon **dried thyme**, crumbled
- ½ teaspoon **salt**
- ¼ teaspoon freshly **ground pepper**

Roasted Root Vegetables

CHAPTER 6

Best Salsas, Dressings, and Sauces

Tropical Bean Salsa

Sweet mango and canned black beans star in this quick-fix salsa that's ideal to serve with grilled steak, chicken, or fish. Diced red onion and bell pepper add color and texture.

In a medium bowl, combine the onion, mango, bell pepper, corn, beans, lime juice, salt, and pepper. Let stand 5 minutes to allow the flavors to blend. Stir in the cilantro.

PER SERVING (ABOUT ¾ CUP): 97 Cal, 1 g Fat, 0 g Sat Fat, 0 g Trans Fat, 0 mg Chol, 209 mg Sod, 22 g Carb, 4 g Fib, 3 g Prot, 25 mg Calc. *POINTS* value: *1*.

★

★ **tip** Select mangoes with unblemished, yellow skin blushed with red. Ripe mangoes will yield to gentle pressure and emit a perfumed fragrance. Avoid fruit with shriveled or black-speckled skin.

MAKES 4 SERVINGS ✴ ⏱ ➹

1 **red onion**, diced

1 **mango**, peeled, pitted, and diced

½ **red bell pepper**, seeded and diced

½ cup fresh or thawed frozen **corn kernels**

½ cup canned **black beans**, rinsed and drained

2 tablespoons **fresh lime juice**

¼ teaspoon **salt**

⅛ teaspoon freshly **ground pepper**

2 tablespoons chopped **fresh cilantro** or **parsley**

Clockwise from top: Tropical Bean Salsa, Double-Pepper Salsa, Zesty Tomato Salsa

Double-Pepper Salsa

Sweet red bell peppers partner with fiery jalapeño peppers in this zesty mix that will perk up many foods. Use as a dip for crudités, a topping for chicken or fish, or a chunky dressing for salads.

Put the bell pepper, onion, jalapeños, and garlic in a food processor; pulse until fairly smooth. Transfer to a medium bowl; stir in the tomatoes, cilantro, lime juice, salt, and pepper. Cover and refrigerate at least 1 hour before serving to allow the flavors to blend.

PER SERVING (ABOUT ⅔ CUP): 54 Cal, 1 g Fat, 0 g Sat Fat, 0 g Trans Fat, 0 mg Chol, 304 mg Sod, 12 g Carb, 3 g Fib, 2 g Prot, 21 mg Calc. **POINTS** value: *1*.

★

★ **tip** This salsa is in the medium-to-hot range. Experiment with different peppers to change the level of spiciness. A rule of thumb: The smaller or pointier the chile pepper, the hotter it will be.

MAKES 4 SERVINGS

1 **red bell pepper,** seeded and coarsely chopped

1 **onion,** coarsely chopped

1–2 **jalapeño peppers,** seeded and minced (wear gloves to prevent irritation)

2 **garlic cloves**

8 **plum tomatoes,** diced

2 tablespoons chopped **fresh cilantro**

2 tablespoons **fresh lime** or **lemon juice**

½ teaspoon **salt**

¼ teaspoon freshly **ground pepper**

Zesty Tomato Salsa

Once you've made your own salsa and discovered how easy it is, there's no going back to the jarred stuff. What's more, this recipe is as delicious with fresh tomatoes as with canned (if using canned, reduce the salt to ¼ teaspoon), so it can be enjoyed any time of year. If the chopped onion is particularly pungent, rinse it first in a fine sieve under cold running water, pat dry with paper towels, then add to the remaining ingredients. That will eliminate its harshness.

1. On a cutting board, sprinkle the salt over the garlic. Mash to a paste with the flat side of a knife.

2. In a small bowl, combine the mashed garlic, the tomatoes, onion, cilantro, jalapeño, and lime juice. Let stand at least ½ hour before serving to allow the flavors to blend.

PER SERVING (⅓ CUP): 17 Cal, 0 g Fat, 0 g Sat Fat, 0 g Trans Fat, 0 mg Chol, 200 mg Sod, 4 g Carb, 1 g Fib, 1 g Prot, 6 mg Calc. **POINTS** value: **0.**

★
★ **tip** When the garlic is being mashed, the salt absorbs much of the juice and prevents the garlic from sticking to the knife. This salsa can be refrigerated, tightly covered, for up to 2 days.

MAKES 6 SERVINGS 🔥 ✴ 🕐 🌶

½ teaspoon **salt**

1 **garlic clove**, minced

2 large ripe **tomatoes**, seeded and finely chopped, or 2 cups drained whole canned tomatoes, finely chopped

1 small **onion**, finely chopped

2–3 tablespoons finely chopped **fresh cilantro**

1–2 **jalapeño peppers**, seeded and finely chopped (wear gloves to prevent irritation)

2 teaspoons **fresh lime juice**

Everyday Vinaigrette

Instead of reaching for the bottled stuff, make a batch of this foolproof dressing. Once you taste it, you'll use it frequently—for tossing with greens or veggies or for marinating chicken or seafood. Vary the taste and add 2 teaspoons minced fresh herbs—thyme, tarragon, chives, parsley, or any combination—if desired.

1. Sprinkle the salt over the garlic on a cutting board. Mash to a paste with the flat side of a heavy knife.

2. Combine the mashed garlic, the broth, vinegars, oil, and shallots in a small jar with a tight-fitting lid. Cover and shake well.

PER SERVING (2 TABLESPOONS): 50 Cal, 5 g Fat, 1 g Sat Fat, 0 g Trans Fat, 0 mg Chol, 322 mg Sod, 2 g Carb, 0 g Fib, 0 g Prot, 4 mg Calc. *POINTS* value: *1*.

★

★ **tip** Serve the dressing immediately or cover and refrigerate for up to 1 week. You may use white-wine vinegar instead of the red.

MAKES 8 SERVINGS

- 1 teaspoon **salt**

- 2 small **garlic cloves**, minced

- 6 tablespoons reduced-sodium **chicken broth**

- ¼ cup **balsamic vinegar**

- ¼ cup **red-wine vinegar**

- 2 tablespoons + 2 teaspoons **extra-virgin olive oil**

- 2 **shallots**, very finely chopped

Thick 'n' Creamy Herb Dressing

Watercress, dill, and chives give this dressing its fresh herbaceous taste and emerald-green hue, while the cottage cheese, milk, and mayonnaise contribute to its creamy texture. Toss with your favorite greens or serve as a dip for shrimp.

Place all of the ingredients in a blender or mini–food processor and pulse until smooth. Thin with 1 or 2 tablespoons of water if necessary. Cover and refrigerate at least ½ hour or up to 2 days to allow the flavors to blend.

PER SERVING (2 TABLESPOONS): 20 Cal, 0 g Fat, 0 g Sat Fat, 0 g Trans Fat, 1 mg Chol, 98 mg Sod, 2 g Carb, 0 g Fib, 3 g Prot, 27 mg Calc. **POINTS** value: **1**.

MAKES 6 SERVINGS

- ½ cup **fat-free cottage cheese**
- ¼ cup packed **watercress** or flat-leaf **parsley**
- 3 tablespoons **fat-free milk**
- 2 tablespoons **fresh lemon juice**
- 1 tablespoon chopped **fresh dill**
- 1 tablespoon minced **fresh chives**
- 1 tablespoon **fat-free mayonnaise**
- 1 small **garlic clove**, minced

Roasted-Garlic Salad Dressing

If you think yogurt dressings are boring, this recipe, featuring sweet roasted garlic and zesty chives, may change your mind. The garlic can be roasted several days ahead and refrigerated, cutting the prep time to just a matter of minutes.

1. Preheat the oven to 350°F. Wrap the garlic in foil and roast until soft and fragrant, 45–60 minutes. When cool enough to handle, separate the cloves.

2. Squeeze the garlic from the cloves into a blender or food processor. Add the water, ricotta, and yogurt; puree. Transfer to a bowl then stir in the chives, salt, and pepper. Cover and refrigerate at least 2 hours to allow the flavors to blend. Stir again before serving.

PER SERVING (¼ CUP): 54 Cal, 0 g Fat, 0 g Sat Fat, 0 g Trans Fat, 6 mg Chol, 348 mg Sod, 8 g Carb, 0 g Fib, 5 g Prot, 127 mg Calc. **POINTS** value: **1.**

MAKES 4 SERVINGS

- 1 small **garlic bulb**
- 2 tablespoons warm **water**
- ½ cup **fat-free ricotta cheese**
- ¼ cup plain **fat-free yogurt**
- 2 tablespoons finely chopped **fresh chives**
- ½ teaspoon **salt**
- ¼ teaspoon freshly **ground pepper**

Tuscan Herb Vinaigrette

This dressing needs to marinate overnight to allow the full flavor of the basil, lemon zest, garlic, and oregano to develop. Up the garlic to a couple of cloves if you're so inclined, and if you have a garlic press handy, by all means use it.

Combine all of the ingredients in a jar with a tight-fitting lid. Cover and shake well. Refrigerate overnight. Shake again before serving.

PER SERVING (1 ½ TABLESPOONS): 23 Cal, 2 g Fat, 0 g Sat Fat, 0 g Trans Fat, 0 mg Chol, 330 mg Sod, 1 g Carb, 0 g Fib, 0 g Prot, 4 mg Calc. *POINTS* value: *1*.

MAKES 8 SERVINGS

- ½ cup reduced-sodium **chicken broth**

- 2 tablespoons chopped **fresh basil**, or 1 teaspoon dried

- 2 tablespoons **white-wine vinegar**

- 1 tablespoon + 1 teaspoon **extra-virgin olive oil**

- 1 teaspoon grated **lemon zest**

- 1 teaspoon **salt**

- 1 **garlic clove**, minced

- ½ teaspoon **dried oregano**, crumbled

- ¼ teaspoon freshly **ground pepper**

Cucumber-Mint Raita

Just as sour cream can temper the heat of your favorite chili, so can *raita*, a traditional condiment made with yogurt, spices, and various chopped vegetables. Designed as a cooling counterbalance for spicy Indian dishes, *raita's* flavors will improve if the condiment is refrigerated in an airtight container overnight and served the next day. *Raita* is also great as an appetizer, served with crudités.

1. Spoon the yogurt into a coffee filter or a cheesecloth-lined strainer placed over a bowl. Let stand 20 minutes. Discard the liquid.

2. Combine the strained yogurt, cucumbers, jalapeño, mint, cumin, salt, and coriander in a medium bowl.

PER SERVING (¼ CUP): 24 Cal, 0 g Fat, 0 g Sat Fat, 0 g Trans Fat, 1 mg Chol, 169 mg Sod, 5 g Carb, 1 g Fib, 2 g Prot, 60 mg Calc. **POINTS** value: **0**.

★

★ **tip** *Raita* will remain fresh and flavorful, covered and refrigerated, for up to 1 week.

MAKES 12 SERVINGS 🗱 🥕

- 2 cups plain **fat-free yogurt**
- 2 **cucumbers**, peeled, seeded, grated, and squeezed dry
- ¼ **jalapeño pepper**, seeded and finely chopped (wear gloves to prevent irritation)
- 2 tablespoons chopped **fresh mint**
- 1 teaspoon ground **cumin**
- ¾ teaspoon **salt**
- ¼ teaspoon ground **coriander**

Roasted Red-Pepper Sauce

To achieve the most intense flavor, we roast sweet bell peppers, then puree them with extra-virgin olive oil, garlic, and sherry-wine vinegar. The result is a highly versatile sauce that can accompany everything from pasta and baked potatoes to roasted vegetables, poultry, or fish. You might like to make a double batch and refrigerate half for up to 1 week to use as a dip for crudités.

1. Preheat the broiler. Line a baking sheet with foil and place the bell peppers on it. Broil 5 inches from the heat, turning frequently with tongs, until the skins blister, about 15 minutes. Transfer the peppers to a counter and wrap in the foil. Let steam for about 15 minutes. When cool enough to handle, peel them, discard the seeds, and place the peppers in a blender or food processor.

2. Heat the oil in a small skillet over medium heat. Add the garlic and cook, stirring constantly, until lightly golden, 1–2 minutes. Remove the skillet from the heat and stir in the basil. Transfer the mixture to the blender with the bell peppers. Add the vinegar, salt, and pepper; process until smooth.

PER SERVING (¼ CUP): 67 Cal, 4 g Fat, 1 g Sat Fat, 0 g Trans Fat, 0 mg Chol, 294 mg Sod, 9 g Carb, 2 g Fib, 1 g Prot, 19 mg Calc. *POINTS* value: *1*.

MAKES 4 SERVINGS

- 3 large **red bell peppers**
- 1 tablespoon **extra-virgin olive oil**
- 3 **garlic cloves**, minced
- ½ teaspoon **dried basil**
- 2 teaspoons **sherry-wine vinegar**
- ½ teaspoon **salt**
- ⅛ teaspoon freshly **ground pepper**

Oven-Roasted Tomato Sauce

Oven-Roasted Tomato Sauce

Whether you are fortunate enough to start with a bumper crop of peak-season tomatoes or not, roasting is a guaranteed method to coax out their full flavor. We roast the tomatoes with sweet Vidalia onion, so there's no need to add sugar.

1. Adjust the racks to divide the oven into thirds. Preheat the oven to 375°F. Spray 2 large nonstick baking pans with olive oil nonstick spray.

2. Arrange the tomatoes and onion in single layers on the pans. Sprinkle with the vinegar, garlic, salt, and pepper, then spray lightly with the nonstick spray. Roast, switching the pans from one shelf to the other halfway through the cooking time, until the tomatoes and onion are lightly browned and have an intense, sweet aroma, 50–55 minutes.

3. Transfer the tomatoes and onion to a food processor and pulse until the mixture is combined but still somewhat chunky.

PER SERVING (½ CUP): 39 Cal, 1 g Fat, 0 g Sat Fat, 0 g Trans Fat, 0 mg Chol, 208 mg Sod, 9 g Carb, 2 g Fib, 2 g Prot, 13 mg Calc. *POINTS* value: *0.*

★

★ **tip** Try this flavorful sauce over whole-wheat fusilli (1 cup cooked pasta for each serving will increase the *POINTS* value by 4).

MAKES 8 SERVINGS

3 pounds (about 18) **plum tomatoes,** cut in quarters lengthwise

1 large **Vidalia onion,** halved lengthwise, then sliced crosswise

1 tablespoon **balsamic vinegar**

3 **garlic cloves,** minced

¾ teaspoon **salt**

¼ teaspoon freshly **ground pepper**

Favorite Tomato Sauce

This flavorful concoction beats jarred sauces (which are often laden with salt and sugar). Oregano is the herb of choice here, but you can substitute an equal amount of fresh or dried basil. This recipe makes a generous batch, plenty to use for pizzas, pasta dishes, or to serve with meat, or fish.

1. Heat the oil in a large nonstick Dutch oven over medium heat. Add the onions and garlic and cook, stirring frequently, until golden, about 10 minutes.

2. Add the tomatoes, tomato paste, oregano, salt, ground pepper, and crushed red pepper (if using); bring to a boil. Reduce the heat and simmer, uncovered, until the flavors are blended and the sauce is slightly thickened, about 25 minutes.

PER SERVING (½ CUP): 48 Cal, 2 g Fat, 0 g Sat Fat, 0 g Trans Fat, 0 mg Chol, 110 mg Sod, 9 g Carb, 2 g Fib, 2 g Prot, 15 mg Calc. **POINTS** value: *1*.

★
★ **tip** Refrigerate the sauce for up to 3 days or freeze it for up to 3 months.

MAKES 12 SERVINGS

1 tablespoon **extra-virgin olive oil**

2 **onions**, finely chopped

4 **garlic cloves**, minced

3 pounds (about 18) **plum tomatoes**, chopped, or 2 (28-ounce) cans Italian plum tomatoes, drained and chopped

2 tablespoons **tomato paste**

1 tablespoon finely chopped **fresh oregano**, or 1 teaspoon dried

½ teaspoon **salt**

¼ teaspoon freshly **ground pepper**

⅛ teaspoon **crushed red pepper** (optional)

Rich Brown Sauce

This classic sauce is ideal to serve with roast beef, beef tenderloin, or steak. The recipe can easily be doubled or tripled so you can have some on hand for last-minute meals. Cool and transfer to plastic containers, then refrigerate for up to 3 days or freeze for up to 3 months.

1. Heat the oil in a medium saucepan over medium heat. Add the onion, carrot, celery, shallot, and garlic. Cook, stirring frequently, until the vegetables are browned, about 7 minutes. Add the broth, tomato paste, parsley, and thyme; simmer until reduced to 2½ cups, about 25 minutes.

2. Strain the vegetables, then return the sauce to the saucepan. Discard the vegetables. Return the sauce to a simmer and cook until reduced to 1½ cups, 6–7 minutes. Stir in the salt and pepper.

PER SERVING (¼ CUP): 23 Cal, 2 g Fat, 0 g Sat Fat, 0 g Trans Fat, 0 mg Chol, 324 mg Sod, 1 g Carb, 0 g Fib, 2 g Prot, 0 mg Calc. **POINTS** value: **1**.

★
★ **tip** To make this a *demi-glace*—a thick, intense base for other sauces—omit the salt and pepper and reduce the sauce to a syrupy consistency.

MAKES 6 SERVINGS

2 teaspoons **olive oil**

1 medium **onion**, finely chopped

1 small **carrot**, chopped

½ **celery** stalk, chopped

1 **shallot**, finely chopped

1 **garlic clove**, minced

3 cups reduced-sodium **beef broth**

1 tablespoon **tomato paste**

3 sprigs **fresh parsley**

1 sprig **fresh thyme**, or ½ teaspoon dried

¼ teaspoon **salt**

⅛ teaspoon freshly **ground pepper**

Creamy Horseradish Sauce

If you're looking to perk up the flavor of burgers or steak, a dollop of this zesty sauce will amply do the job.

Combine the horseradish, yogurt, sour cream, mustard, Worcestershire sauce, and pepper in a medium bowl. Stir in the parsley just before serving. Serve at once or cover and refrigerate for up to 2 days.

PER SERVING (3 TABLESPOONS): 27 Cal, 0 g Fat, 0 g Sat Fat, 0 g Trans Fat, 1 mg Chol, 101 mg Sod, 5 g Carb, 1 g Fib, 2 g Prot, 56 mg Calc. *POINTS* value: *0.*

★

★ **tip** This sauce is great with a burger, lettuce, and tomato in a whole-wheat bun. Increase the *POINTS* value by 4 for each cooked, extra-lean 3-ounce beef patty and increase the *POINTS* value by 3 for each 2-ounce dinner roll.

MAKES 8 SERVINGS 🔥 ✳ 🕒

½ cup drained prepared **horseradish**

½ cup plain **fat-free yogurt**

⅓ cup **fat-free sour cream**

2 teaspoons **whole-grain mustard**

½ teaspoon **Worcestershire sauce**

⅛ teaspoon freshly **ground pepper**

2 tablespoons chopped **fresh parsley**

Creamy Horseradish Sauce

About Our Recipes

We make every effort to ensure that you will have success with our recipes. For best results and for nutritional accuracy, please keep the following guidelines in mind:

- All recipes feature approximate nutritional information; our recipes are analyzed for Calories (Cal), Total Fat (Fat), Saturated Fat (Sat Fat), Trans Fat (Trans Fat), Cholesterol (Chol), Sodium (Sod), Carbohydrates (Carb), Dietary Fiber (Fib), Protein (Prot), and Calcium (Calc).

- Nutritional information for recipes that include meat, fish, and poultry are based on cooked skinless boneless portions (unless otherwise stated), with the fat trimmed as specified in the recipe.

- All recipes in this book have been developed for Weight Watchers members who are following the **Core Plan** on the **TurnAround** program. We also include *POINTS* values so you can use the recipes if you are following the **Flex Plan** on the program. *POINTS* values are assigned based on calories, fat (grams), and fiber (grams) provided for a serving size of a recipe.

- Before serving, divide foods—including any vegetables, sauce, or accompaniments—into portions of equal size according to the designated number of servings per recipe.

- Any substitutions made to the ingredients will alter the "Per serving" nutritional information and may affect the *POINTS* value.

- It is implied that all greens in recipes should be washed or rinsed.

- All herbs called for are fresh, not dried, unless otherwise specified.

Dry and Liquid Measurement Equivalents

If you are converting the recipes in this book to metric measurements, use the following chart as a guide.

TEASPOONS	TABLESPOONS	CUPS	FLUID OUNCES
3 teaspoons	1 tablespoon		½ fluid ounce
6 teaspoons	2 tablespoons	⅛ cup	1 fluid ounce
8 teaspoons	2 tablespoons plus 2 teaspoons	⅙ cup	
12 teaspoons	4 tablespoons	¼ cup	2 fluid ounces
15 teaspoons	5 tablespoons	⅓ cup minus 1 teaspoon	
16 teaspoons	5 tablespoons plus 1 teaspoon	⅓ cup	
18 teaspoons	6 tablespoons	¼ cup plus 2 tablespoons	3 fluid ounces
24 teaspoons	8 tablespoons	½ cup	4 fluid ounces
30 teaspoons	10 tablespoons	½ cup plus 2 tablespoons	5 fluid ounces
32 teaspoons	10 tablespoons plus 2 teaspoons	⅔ cup	
36 teaspoons	12 tablespoons	¾ cup	6 fluid ounces
42 teaspoons	14 tablespoons	1 cup minus 2 tablespoons	7 fluid ounces
45 teaspoons	15 tablespoons	1 cup minus 1 tablespoon	
48 teaspoons	16 tablespoons	1 cup	8 fluid ounces

VOLUME	
¼ teaspoon	1 milliliter
½ teaspoon	2 milliliters
1 teaspoon	5 milliliters
1 tablespoon	15 milliliters
2 tablespoons	30 milliliters
3 tablespoons	45 milliliters
¼ cup	60 milliliters
⅓ cup	80 milliliters
½ cup	120 milliliters
⅔ cup	160 milliliters
¾ cup	175 milliliters
1 cup	240 milliliters
1 quart	950 milliliters

LENGTH	
1 inch	25 millimeters
1 inch	2.5 centimeters

OVEN TEMPERATURE

250°F	120°C	400°F	200°C
275°F	140°C	425°F	220°C
300°F	150°C	450°F	230°C
325°F	160°C	475°F	250°C
350°F	180°C	500°F	260°C
375°F	190°C	525°F	270°C

WEIGHT	
1 ounce	30 grams
¼ pound	120 grams
½ pound	240 grams
1 pound	480 grams

NOTE: Measurement of less than ⅛ teaspoon is considered a dash or a pinch. Metric volume measurements are approximate.

Roasting Basics

Roasting is one of the easiest, low-fat methods for cooking meat and poultry, especially if you follow these guidelines:

• Preheat the oven to the temperature stated in the recipe (usually 325°–350°F).

• Pat the meat dry with paper towels and season as directed. Place the meat or poultry on a rack in a shallow roasting pan. Tent poultry loosely with foil, if desired; do not cover meat.

• Think of the cooking time as a starting point to check the roast. The cooking time depends on many variables: whether the roast is bone-in or boned, whether your bird is stuffed or not, and how large it is. For example, a stuffed 20-pound turkey or a 3-pound boneless rib eye roast should take about 13 minutes per pound, while an unstuffed 1-pound Cornish hen or a 5-pound brisket will take 35 to 45 minutes per pound. Use the times specified in the recipe, or start checking for doneness after roasting 15 to 20 minutes per pound.

• The safest and most accurate way of determining when the roast is cooked sufficiently is with an instant-read thermometer. Insert the thermometer into the thickest part of the roast or the thigh of whole poultry; be sure the thermometer is not touching bone. The heat-reading element is about 1 inch from the tip. To ensure an accurate reading, insert the thermometer up to the small indentation. See the chart (opposite) for safe cooking temperatures.

• When the roast reaches the right temperature, transfer to a cutting board, cover loosely with foil and let stand 10 to 15 minutes before carving. The internal temperature will continue to rise 5 to 10 degrees and the juices will redistribute through the roast.

Beef
medium-rare ....135°F
medium ....150°F
meatloaf ....160°F

Veal   165°F

Chicken & Turkey
thigh................................180°F
breast..............................170°F

Capon
thigh................................180°F

Cornish Game Hens
thigh................................180°F

Pork..............................160°F

Ham
fully-cooked......................140°F
fresh ham ....160°F

Lamb
medium-rare.....................140°F
medium ....155°F

Great Grilling

For those trying to lose weight, the good news is: Grilling has officially become a year-round method for cooking steaks, chicken, pork, fish, vegetables, even fruit. Yet it's important to keep in mind that between enjoying being in the great outdoors, and having fun with friends and family, it's easy to be distracted from the task at hand. As with any kind of cooking, you need to pay attention to the temperature and the cooking time—which means watching the food, controlling the heat, and turning or moving the food as needed. So before you fire up the grill, consider the following tips:

- Get the grate hot enough. Make sure your grill and grate are fully preheated before you start; this can take from 15 to 25 minutes, depending on your grill. Once you've fired up the grill (with the lid open), close the lid so that the grate gets fully heated.

- To test if the grill is hot enough, place your hand a couple of inches above the top of the cooking grate, and count the seconds until the heat of the fire forces you to pull away. If you can't keep it there more than one or two seconds, you've got a hot fire, three seconds is medium-high, and four to five seconds is moderate (the ideal temperature for chicken grilling).

- Spray the grill rack with nonstick cooking spray before you grill. A clean, lightly greased grate helps prevent sticking and burning.

- When you're finished grilling, scrape the still-hot grate clean with a wire grill brush, to get it ready for your next barbecue.

- Keep an instant-read meat thermometer on hand to check for doneness for all meat.

Grilling Meat

- Trim excess fat before cooking to prevent flare-ups.

- Score edges of steaks before grilling to prevent curling.

- Use long-handled tongs to turn meat and poultry (piercing with a fork allows juices to escape).

- Don't forget the herbs. Fresh chopped oregano is particularly delicious paired with beef and fresh rosemary is good with lamb.

- Cook tender cuts of meat (such as rib-eye, T-bone, filet mignon, and sirloin steaks) by first searing them over direct high heat on one side. Turn with tongs and continue to grill, reducing the heat by raising the cooking rack.

Index

Notes

Fruits! apples, appricots, banana², black/blueberries, cherries, grapes, oranges, papaya, peach, pear, plum, strawberries, watermelon

Veggies 0 asparagus, green beans, beets, broccoli, brussel sprouts, cabbage, carrots, cauliflower, celery, corn, cucumber, lettuce, mushrooms, onions, peppers, sm.red potato , greens, spinach, squash, tomatoes, zucchini.

e-tools access code: 1-4-635-2854427384

keep healthy foods home.
eat fruits/veg. & "low points" first
exercise everyday
attend meetings / be positive.

Goals: (148-153#) : portion control,
change junkfood/soda habits.

Everyday
1. It's worth it!   exercise
                           stay w/i point value
2. I can do it!